D1461207

The "Teaching of English" Series

General Editor—Sir Henry Newbolt

SIX MODERN PLAYS

AND TWO OLD PLAYS

FOR LITTLE PLAYERS

No. 164

A. P. HERBERT

From a pen-drawing by E. Heber Thompson.

(After a copyright photograph by **Northcliffe**
Newspapers, Ltd.)

SIX MODERN PLAYS

AND TWO OLD PLAYS
FOR LITTLE PLAYERS

Edited by

JOHN HAMPDEN

THOMAS NELSON AND SONS, Ltd.

LONDON, EDINBURGH, AND NEW YORK

First published May 1931
Reprinted September 1931

CONTENTS

SIX MODERN PLAYS

TWO OLD PLAYS

COMMENTARY

*The six modern plays are fully protected by copy-
right. The terms on which performances may be
given are stated in the Acting Notes.*

SIX MODERN PLAYS

PREFACE

POETRY and adventure, laughter and the spirit of
worship, come together in this little book, and the
players for whom it is intended will find no incon-
gruity in the meeting. All the plays have been chosen
for their appeal to actors and readers of about eleven
or twelve years old, as well as for their dramatic and
literary merit, so that the present volume takes its
place between the same editor's *Ballads and Ballad-
Plays* and *Eight Modern Plays for Juniors*, as part
of a carefully graduated course in the study of drama.
This course leads up to the plays of Shakespeare,
Sheridan, and others of our classical dramatists, and
provides for a return to modern drama with *Nine
Modern Plays* and *Ten Modern Plays*, both in this
series, and *Four Modern Plays*, published in " The
Nelson Playbooks " (see page 216), the last three
volumes having been planned for older pupils, and
having proved very popular also with adult dramatic
societies.

The editor wishes to express his thanks to the
following authors and publishers for permission to
reprint their plays :

Mrs. Naomi Mitchison and Mr. Jonathan Cape for
Elfen Hill ; Mrs. Eric Streatfeild and Messrs. Curwen
and Sons for *Peter and the Clock* ; Mr. John Drinkwater and Messrs. Sidgwick and Jackson for *Robin
Hood and the Pedlar*, from the author's " Collected

Plays "; Mr. Graham Robertson and Messrs. William
Heinemann, Ltd., for *Archibald* ; Mr. A. P. Herbert
and the Oxford University Press for *Fat King Melon* ;
and Miss Elizabeth A. McFadden and Messrs. Samuel
French for *Why the Chimes Rang*.

J. H.

ELFEN HILL

By Naomi Mitchison

CHARACTERS

QUEEN MIRANDA.
PRINCE GARAMOND.
THE OLD NURSE.
THE CHAMBERLAIN.
THE PAGES.
THE ELF KING.
THE ELF GIRL.
THE ELF BOY.
THE OTHER ELF BOY.
THE ELF CHILDREN.
THE NIXIE.

SCENES

I. Queen Miranda's Palace.   II. Rushy Brook.
III. The Elfen Hill.

ELFEN HILL

SCENE I

A room in Queen Miranda's palace.

In this scene the green back-cloth, against which the whole play is to be done, might have large golden crowns or fleurs-de-lis tacked against it. There is a chair to one side. Queen Miranda is walking up and down in her dress of white and gold brocade; she wears a short cape of white fur, gold slippers, and a gold crown, heavily jewelled. In the chair sits her Old Nurse; she wears a long grey dress with a white coif and white cuffs and apron; she is sewing at a long piece of stuff which lies in her lap, scarlet and gold and green. The Queen twists her fingers impatiently together as she walks, and at last flings out both arms towards her Old Nurse.

> *Queen Miranda.* Oh Nursie, stop your sewing
> now,
> Lay by your red and green :
> For oh I'm weary of ruling here
> Where I am a crownéd Queen !
>
> For I must sit all day on a throne
> —A weary throne to me—
> When I would be out in the good green wood
> With the dun deer running free !

For I must keep a crown on my head
—A weary weight to wear—
When I would be out on Broomy Knowe
That is so fine and fair !

For I must keep a tongue in my head
—A tongue that's not my own—
To talk with the King of a far countree
That's come to court and marry with me,
And he as ugly as man can be
With a heart as cold as a stone,
When I would be out by Rushy Brook
And walking all alone !

    Nurse [*laying by her work*]. Oh, mistress, be not
           vexéd so—
An ill thing to be seen !
There's many a maid that envies you,
A robed and crownéd Queen.

And though the wild wood's fair in spring,
In winter it is cold ;
And if your crown's a weary weight,
Yet 'tis of finest gold.

    Queen. Oh, Nursie, let them take my crown
If me they envy so,
And I will go to the Bonny Brook
Where the rushes stand a-row.

Oh I will braid my yellow hair
A little abune my bree,
And I will kilt my silken skirt
A little abune my knee,
And I'll be off to Rushy Brook
As fast as I can flee !

    Abune, Above.   *Bree*, Brow.

Nurse [*rising*]. Oh, think you shame, my mistress
  dear,
That any such thing should say,
When you must marry a noble King
Has come from far away !

Queen [*half to herself*]. Oh, if I had but one
  brother
'Tis he should be a King,
And leave me free for the leafy shawes
Where the small birds do sing !

Nurse [*after a moment*]. You were a babe when
  Prince Garamond
Was taken from us all,
The day that he was six years old,
A bonny boy and a tall ;
For there came a man in a green mantle
That carried a golden ball.

He kicked the ball, and tossed the ball,
Your brother came too near ;
That man he caught him in his arms,
Of us he had no fear,
But snatcht away your one brother
That was so small and dear.

Mistress, it was the Elfen King
Away your brother bore,
And has kept him fast in Elfen Hill
For twelve years, and more.

Queen. But was there none to bring him home
Out of the Elfen Hill ?

Nurse. Nay, there was no man bold enough,
Nor no man had the skill.

For they who go to Elfen Land
Must neither drink nor eat,
Nor wear the elf combs in their hair
Nor the elf shoes on their feet.

The Elfen King is a riddling King,
His riddles are all his own,
And who knows not the fair answer
Is turnéd to a stone.

[*A flourish of trumpets! Two little Pages in
white and gold come in, carrying gilt trumpets. After them comes the Chamberlain;
he wears a cloak of black and red, with wide,
fur-edged sleeves, something like a judge's
robes, but with just a slight academic sug-
gestion; and his cap of office should make
one think of a rather gayer mortar-board.
His voice is distinctly authoritative.*]

The Pages [*together*]. Her Majesty the Queen!
Her Majesty the Queen!
The beautiful,
The dutiful,
The most constitutional Queen!

[*The Chamberlain now advances with a stiff and
chilly bow.*]

Chamberlain. Her Majesty the Queen will be
pleased to receive the nineteen Ambassadors from
Allantopolis.
Queen [*stamping*]. Her Majesty the Queen will
not be pleased!
Chamberlain. Her Majesty will be pleased to
understand that if any of the nineteen Ambassadors are offended, the Allantopolitans will im-

mediately occupy the Royal Mustard Mines and an Ultimatum will be sent off in the usual form.

Queen. Oh—very well.

[*She shrugs her shoulders and prepares to do her duty.*]

Chamberlain. May I be permitted to observe that Her Majesty's royal crown is verging towards Her Majesty's right eyebrow ?

Queen. I've never known such a crown for taking into its head to go crooked ! Bother the crown !   [*Her Nurse puts it straight.*]

Chamberlain. Her Majesty will be pleased to omit the word " bother " from her vocabulary ; Her Majesty is permitted to make use of the expression " dear me." [*She puts out her tongue at him ; he looks away and continues frigidly.*] Her Majesty will be interested to learn that Her Majesty's ministers are at present engaged in deciding the date of Her Majesty's august marriage.

Queen. Oh, you aren't going to make me marry that horrible old king with a face like a turnip !

Chamberlain [*at last moved*]. Your Majesty ! I am pained—deeply pained. Your Majesty's never-too-much-to-be-revered-in-the-comparatively-near-future Consort ! Please, please !

[*He bows her out. The Pages follow.*]

CURTAIN

SCENE II

Rushy Brook.

Of course the nicest thing would be for some one to paint a back-cloth of straight rushes ; it oughtn't to

*be very difficult. But failing that there should be
two or three jars of long rushes on the floor, and
perhaps a couple of yellow flags or water docks ; but
the rushes must be really green, not old, dried-up
bulrushes out of the boxroom. Perhaps they could
even be made of ribbon in two or three shades of
green ; they ought to be just long and straight and
damp-looking. Anything in the way of moss or
green plants would be nice, but if there are too many
they take a long time to arrange, and get mixed up
with the properties. At the back there should be a
log or a green bank ; but if there is nothing else
some big green cushions would look quite well.*

*On this bank sits the Nixie ; she wears a trailing
dress of grey and grey-blue and watery green with
knotted water-weeds hanging from her shoulders :
she has water-lilies or shell shapes in her hair, and a
long silver wand by her side. As she sits, she combs
her hair with a silver comb.*

Nixie. There's a stream whose waters flow
Gently quick or softly slow.
Birds along that river's brink
Dip and sprinkle, preen and drink ;
Under every bank are seen
Flag-leaves lifting smooth and green,
In the sand of every pool
Flag-roots lying white and cool.
Through the drifting afternoon
Rises up a little moon ;
Shines she with her growing light,
On the water laughing white.

Oh my moon, and oh my stream,
Shadows changing in my dream,
(8,554)

While I sit and comb my hair
Tangled by the twining air.

[*Queen Miranda runs forward, her hair flying;
she holds up her dress with both hands. The
Nixie draws back frightened, and hides,
watching the Queen.*]

Queen. Oh here I am,
　　　And here I am
　　　Among the rushes green;
　　　Where the brook flows
　　　Nobody knows
　　　That I'm a runaway Queen!

[*She takes off her crown and lays it down. The
Nixie peeps from her hiding-place.*]

Nixie. Why do you cast your golden crown,
Lady, lady?

Queen. It weighs so much that it weighs me
　　　down,
Nixie, Nixie!

[*She takes off her shoes and stockings, or, better,
she takes off her shoes and has no stockings
under them. The Nixie comes a few steps
forward.*]

Nixie. Why do you cast your golden shoes,
Lady, lady?

Queen. Who would wear them if she could
　　　choose,
Nixie, Nixie!

[*She takes off her upper dress of gold and fur; it
unfastens at neck and waist, and leaves her in*

[*a plain bodice and long petticoat of silver
striped with gold.*]

Nixie. Why do you cast your silken dress,
Lady, lady ?

Queen. See, when I dance, it's one thing less,
Nixie, Nixie !

[*She takes a few dance steps ; the Nixie comes
quite near and reaches out a hand towards the
crown.*]

Nixie. May I put on your crown and dress,
And the shoes all shimmer, princess, princess ?

Queen. Yes, if you like them, Nixie, yes !

[*The Nixie picks them up and caresses the gold
and silver with her long hands.*]

Nixie. Oh let me take them, princess dear,
Down to my home in the waters clear !
Oh let me keep them, night and noon,
The happiest Nixie under the moon !
Oh let me keep them, then you can run
The dancingest princess under the sun !

[*She rubs her cheek against them, looking up
sideways at the Queen.*]

Queen. Why, you may keep them if you will,
Nixie, Nixie, gentle and still.
Ten gold crowns in my palace lie,
Ninety dresses to please my eye,
Fifty slippers that pinch my toes,
Waiting for me in golden rows !

Nixie. I will give you my wand of silver,
Silver magic for a princess dear ;

This will open the Elfen doorway,
Only go to it, never fear,
Only strike with the wand of silver
Saying " Doorway : know thy key ! "
Three times say to it " Doorway, doorway,
Elfen doorway, open to me ! "

[*She gives her the silver wand, pointing the way*.]

Queen. Nixie, where is the Elfen doorway ?

Nixie. Go till you see a round green hill ;
Where there's an ash and oak together
There will the doorway open still.

Queen. Oh I will run there, Nixie, Nixie,
Gentle Nixie of Rushy Brook !

Nixie. All good luck to you, princess, princess,
She will find who has wit to look !

CURTAIN

SCENE III

Inside the Elfen Hill.

*Here there should be just the plain green curtain,
but if possible divided in the centre to make an
entrance, and there should be two or three steps in
front of it. If it were done in a real theatre, a
curtain shaped like a low arch would be dropped in
front, so that it would look as if one were seeing into
a cove. The lights might have green or red shades
over them. On the right, Prince Garamond is playing chess at a little table with an Elf Boy ; another*

*leans over his shoulder, watching the game.   The Elf
Boys wear short tunics of metallic green, edged with
scales of blue or red ; either they have bare legs or
else tight green leggings ; green fillets round their
dark hair.   Prince Garamond alone in the Elfen
Hill wears a white doublet edged with white fur,
white silk stockings, and silver-buckled shoes.   His
hair should be fair and curly, and he has a small
sword at his side.   Sitting on the steps, centre, is an
Elf Girl, all in green, with a long, many-pointed
skirt ; her arms are bare and she has a little, three-
stringed harp.   Right in front, and a little to the
left, two Elf Children sit on the ground, playing with
a green tortoise ; they are all in green too.   The Elf
Girl takes up the harp and sings ; the others go on
playing.*

[*Air :* " Sellenger's Round."]

Elf Girl.   Oh merry it is in Elfen Hill
              (With a link-a-down and a day),
              Oh merry to feast and merry to dance,
              And at the ball to play.

              Oh they that live in Elfen Hill
              Fear neither rain nor frost,
              And here the thing is found again
              That otherwhere were lost.

              And here's no end to comeliness,
              And here's no end to play,
              Oh merry it is in Elfen Hill
              (With a link-a-down and a day).

[*She lays her harp down.   The Elf Boy at the
    table makes a move and raises his hand.*]

Elf Boy.   I have you, Garamond : check !

Garamond [*after studying the board a moment*].
Yes, and checkmate !
I never saw your Castle till too late.
[*He takes up the pieces.*]
Now, let me set the board for one more game :
King—Queen—and, oh, it always goes the same !
Why not let Pawns be knighted, Knights turn
    King,
And if there's death, then why not marrying ?

Elf Boy [*laughing at him*]. Yes, and let Queens
    sew samplers, Bishops pray !
This chess of yours gets far too real to play !

Garamond. But take the King ! Why, there's
    no king has been
Would stay mured up and waiting on his queen !
Give him his freedom !   Or on either side
We'll have two Kings, and one a traitor King :
When the board's clear before him, let him ride !

Elf Boy. Yes, but, my Garamond, this is no
    new thing,
But only life wearing a different dress !
Why make your play grow earnest, toys grow
    men ?
If you want blood, why set the board for chess ?
You're tired of this.   Shall we play tennis, then ?

Garamond. No, no, not that. Oh, if I only
    knew !

Elf Boy. Well, dance or ride, play bowls, what
    shall we do ?
Shall we make magics ?   Make a horse with wings
To fly up, up with us, until he flings
His hoof against the moon ?   Make three or four

Great peacocks with gold feathers in their tails ?
Remember how we did that once before !
What then ?   A swan ?   A boat with silver sails
On a great lake—

    Garamond.   Oh, I am tired of magic !
Tired of all this making with no skill,
Tired of riding through the Elfen Hill
In rainless forests lit by no real sun,
Where winds are never cold, skies never grey !
Tired of waiting till the day is done,
Tired of song and dance and endless play !

    [*Suddenly the Elf Girl throws back her head,
        shivering.*]

    Elf Girl. Oh, a cold wind blows through me,
        through me,
Oh, like a knife it pierces sore !
I shiver, shiver, down to my hair-tips,
Some one has opened Elfen door !

    [*The Elf Children huddle together, and the Elf
        Boys shiver, standing in front of Garamond.
        Queen Miranda comes in, left, still barefoot
        and crownless, in her long petticoat, holding
        the Nixie's wand.*]

    Queen. Oh here I come,
          And here I come,
          And into Elfen Hill !
          The wand shows me,
          The door knows me,
          And I shall have my will !

    Elf Girl. She is a mortal !

    Elf Boy. She goes barefoot.

Other Elf Boy. Hungry, thirsty,
          Nothing on her head !

[*The Elf Girl takes the combs out of her hair, and
   offers them, smiling, to Queen Miranda.*]

Elf Girl. Mortal, mortal,
        Pretty, pretty mortal,
        Take my combs for
        Your bonny little head !

Queen. I that have thrown my
        Golden crown off,
        Why should I take
        Your combs instead ?

[*The Elf Boy goes up to her, smiling, with a pair
   of emerald-buckled gold shoes.*]

Elf Boy. Mortal, mortal,
        Pretty, pretty mortal,
        Take my shoes for
        Your bonny little feet !

Queen. Nay, I go barefoot,
        Swift-foot, running,
        Feel on my flesh
        The grasses sweet !

[*The other Elf Boy goes up to her, smiling, and
   offers her fruits of all colours on a green dish.*]

Other Elf Boy. Mortal, mortal,
          Pretty, pretty mortal,
          Take my fruits on
          Their bonny little dish !

Queen. I am not hungry,
        Elf Folk, Elf Folk,

Now you must grant me
All I wish !

[*Suddenly there is a great flash of green light, and
the Elf King stands in the opening, centre, at
the top of the steps. He should be tall and
dark, wearing green scale armour, with a
pointed helmet, flickering with green light,
and a queer-shaped sword. Failing this, he
must wear a long, green cloak from neck to
ankle, leaving one arm free.*]

Elf King. Noon-day dark and midnight clear,
There is a doomèd mortal here :
Be she living or be she dead,
Her heart this night shall spice my bread !

Queen. Elf King, you have no power over me !
Elf Girl. She will not take the combs in her
hair.
Elf Boy. She will not wear the shoes on her
feet.
Other Elf Boy. She will not eat nor drink.
Queen. It is another thing I need of you, and
that I will have.
Elf King. Nay, but it was a foolish bird to run
so fast into the snare. Mortal, you must answer
me three riddles.
Queen. And if I do not answer ?
[*The two Elf Boys and the Elf Girl, even the Elf
Children, come close up round her, and
answer all together.*]
All. Her heart this night shall spice our bread !
Elf King. The burden that every man wishes
but he who has it : riddle me that.
Queen [*after a moment*]. That is an easy riddle

to one who knows the answer too well : it is a
crown. [*The Elves look at one another doubtfully.*]

Elf King. Three old men in red cloaks making
chains heavy enough to bind a kingdom, without
hammer or forge : riddle me that.

Queen [*after a moment*]. That I have seen with
my own eyes. They are the judges making laws.

[*The Elves murmur.*]

Elf King. One eye with a long tail helps two
eyes to shut the door in no eyes : riddle me that.

Queen [*at once*]. Elf King, your riddles are
easy ! Only yesterday I saw my old Nurse mend-
ing a coat with needle and thread.

[*The Elves cry out.*]

Elf King. You have answered my riddles ; I
will let you go free out of Elfen Hill.

Queen. Not without that I came to seek !

[*She stretches out her wand ; the Elves cower
away. The Elf King covers his face with
his hand for a moment.*]

Elf King. So be it : choose.

Queen. My choice is short : Garamond !

[*As she calls, Garamond comes towards her slowly,
and looks in her face.*]

Elf Boy. Garamond, stay with us !

Elf Girl. Garamond, remember the song and the
dance !

Elf King. Garamond, do not go where you
must lose your youth !

Queen. Brother, come home.

Garamond [*slowly*]. When I look in your eyes,
sister, I can think of things that have been hidden
for more years than I can tell. I can remember
rain and snow and the sound of the wind on
winter nights : bare boughs and empty nests and

a rusted ploughshare. I can remember faces of old men who had nothing to look forward to, and I can remember sick folk, and a man in chains going to prison. And I can remember a cradle with silk curtains and in the cradle my baby sister ; the cradle stood out on a lawn of green grass with swallows flying over it ; and as the swallows flickered the baby tossed its arms and laughed. And I can remember—oh—oh—the golden ball of the Elf King that burnt my hands !

Queen. Come back with me and grow up and be a King yourself.

Garamond. Shall I have power ?

Queen. It was little enough power I had when I was Queen, but maybe you'll have more. And oh, when you're ruling, brother, do you promise never to bid me marry any old king of a far country that I hate with all my heart !

Garamond. I will come back with you, little sister, and your marriage shall be your own choice.

[*He takes her hand.*]

Queen. Elf Folk, Elf Folk, I have my brother,
My bonny brother who comes with me
Out of the power of Elfen Hill
And all the Elfen Companee !

Elf King. I cannot hold you, Garamond,
When you would go of your own free will ;
But sorely will you think of us
And sadly wish for the Elfen Hill.

Elf Girl. Oh bonny playmate Garamond,
I thought you were mine own ;
Full many a play have we played together,
Now I must play alone.

Elf Boy. Why must you leave us, Garamond,
And why must we be twined ?
You will not find the middle earth
So merry or so kind.

Your sister thinks to love you well,
But not so well as we ;
So bide with us in Elfen Hill
And do not think to flee !

> [*The Elf Folk all stretch out their arms towards
>   him ; but his sister still holds him by the
>   hand.*]

Garamond. Oh Elf Folk love the Elfen Hill
And all that lies within,
But I must love the bonny mid-earth,
For I come of a mortal kin.

So fare you well, my fairy feres,
And think of me no ill,
For I must home with my own sister
That has so muckle skill.

And fare you well, my fairy feres,
And fare you well again !
I must go back to Christentie
With muckle woe and pain.

And fare thee well, thou Elfen Hill,
And merry may'st thou stay,
And fare thee well, thou bonny lass
With whom I used to play !

> [*He throws one arm desperately over his face, and
>   Queen Miranda leads him out. The Elf*

Feres, Comrades.   *Christentie*, Christendom.

*Folk stand together, looking after him. By-
and-by the Elf Girl starts singing again.*]

Elf Girl.   But here's no end to comeliness
            And here's no end to play ;
            Oh merry it is in Elfen Hill
            With a link-a-down—

[*But she throws her harp from her, and on a
sudden the Elf Folk are all weeping.*]

CURTAIN

PETER AND THE CLOCK

By Kitty Barne

CHARACTERS

FANNY, *aged* 14.
PETER, *aged* 9.
VICTORIA, *aged* 8.
MAMMA'S VOICE }
MAID'S VOICE   } *are heard off the stage.*

The action of the play takes place in about the year
1840.

PETER AND THE CLOCK

SCENE.—*A room, comfortably but plainly furnished as a dining-room in the fashion of* 1840. *There is a table against the wall on the right, on which is a big work-basket. One or two straight-backed chairs are pushed underneath it. A big grandfather clock is the most conspicuous feature of the room against the wall on the left. It has a particularly loud tick, which is best achieved by a metronome hidden behind it. A window with ginger-coloured curtains faces you.*

Peter, a boy of nine, is sitting on a rocking-chair, a black wood one with red plush seat and back, rocking busily, and gazing thoughtfully at the clock.

There is a fireplace on the left, beside which Fanny sits. She is about fourteen years old, and is dressed for a party in the height of juvenile fashion, a miniature replica of a grown-up lady. She wears a ball dress of white muslin with low neck and short sleeves, and trousers gathered round her ankles. She sits bolt upright in her straight-backed chair with her skirt over her head to prevent it being crumpled, showing a petticoat covered with little frills; her mittened hands are held stiffly away from her finery, and her feet, in black slippers, are resting carefully on a footstool. Her hair is parted in the middle, elaborately curled, and tied with a blue ribbon.

Victoria, a little girl of eight, stands looking

enviously at her; she wears a dingy little dress of brown alpaca with a black apron; her hair is parted in the middle very smoothly, and tidied away into a net.

Fanny [*hardly able to see through her dress*]. Victoria! Victoria!

Victoria. Yes.

Fanny. Oh, there you are! Pray pick up my handkerchief for me. I've dropped it, and I mustn't get up to pick it up for fear of crumpling my dress. Mamma said so. [*Victoria does so.*] Thank you. [*Proudly, after a slight pause.*] I've had my hair curled with tongs.

Victoria [*enviously*]. Have you? I do wish I could go to parties.

Fanny. A man did it. Mamma had him out of a shop. I expect it will stay in a long time if I put it in curl-papers every night.

Victoria. Why can't I go too?

Fanny. Mamma will not allow you to go to parties till you are twelve; that is her rule.

Victoria. But *why* shouldn't I go now?

Fanny. I expect the negus would make you ill.

Victoria [*hotly*]. Well, you've got to drink Gregory when you come back. I heard you promise to.

Fanny [*calmly*]. Yes, I know. But I shall have a glass of port wine and a biscuit to-morrow morning at eleven and breakfast with mamma.

Victoria. It'll be my turn to wear that sash on Sunday, anyhow, and my turn to sit next to mamma in the pew.

[*She pulls out a chair that was pushed under the table and sits down, her legs crossed.*]

Fanny [*sharply*]. Peter ! Pray stop rocking like that. You know we are not allowed to use that chair. What are you doing ?

Peter [*getting up slowly*]. Thinking.

Fanny. Look out of the window and tell me if the fly is come. I wish it was not a hack cab. Every one has a carriage now. Emily Oldfield's papa has one, with a coachman and a footman and Tiger at the back.

Peter [*pointing to the clock*]. When did he say it might come ?

Fanny [*mystified*]. He ? Who's he ?

Peter. The clock.

Fanny. Oh, Peter, what a funny boy you are ! You speak of the clock as if it was a *gentleman* ! Mamma ordered the fly for six o'clock. We are going to drive Ensign FitzJames with us. [*Complacently.*] I expect he will dance " Sir Roger " with me.

Victoria. He's a grown-up gentleman. He won't dance with *you*.

Fanny. Yes, he will. I danced with a Cornet the last time I went to a party, and he was older. He had lovely whiskers. He took me down to supper . . . twice. I *do* wish I hadn't promised mamma only to go once this time.

[*She sighs, and there is a pause. Peter, meanwhile, has gone to the window and is peeping out behind the curtain.*]

Fanny [*suddenly*]. Victoria ! Oh fie ! What would mamma say if she saw you with your legs crossed like that ? [*She points an accusing finger at her.*]

Victoria [*quickly putting her knees and feet together*]. I . . . I forgot.

(3,554)

3

Fanny. That just shows you're too young for parties. You might do that before a gentleman, and he *would* be shocked.

Victoria. Would he?

Fanny. Of course he would. Dreadfully shocked!

Peter [*coming back from the window*]. There isn't anything at the door, but if the clock said *six* o'clock there wouldn't be yet. He hasn't got to six.

Fanny [*peevishly*]. I'm tired of waiting. I do wish the time would go faster.

Peter [*running over to her and speaking in a dramatic, vehement whisper*]. S-s-sh! Don't let him hear you say that. If he thinks you want him to go fast he will crawl—just to spite you.

Fanny [*looking at him in astonishment*]. Peter! What funny things you do say!

Peter. He will. When I had chicken-pox he went as slowly as he could. He took *hours* to do ten minutes, just because he knew I was in bed. He hurries when I want him to go slow. When I went to the magic lantern he went so fast that I had to come away almost as soon as I got there. He won't let me stay up when I want to, and he won't let me stay in bed when I want to.

Fanny. You talk just as if the clock was alive.

Peter [*with great vehemence*]. So I b'lieve he is. He's alive, and he's wicked. That clock is a *devil*!

[*He shakes his fist at it, and says this terrible word with tremendous emphasis. Fanny is scandalized, and Victoria shocked and decidedly frightened.*]

Fanny } [*together*]. Peter!
Victoria }

Fanny. To think of you saying such a thing !

Peter. It is ! It is ! It's a devil !

Fanny. S-sh! You *mustn't*! It's a . . . swear.
. . . Mamma would swoon if she could hear you.
Only gentlemen may say it ; even the vicar in
church says the " Evil One " ! I think it's a
very good thing that you're going to school to-
morrow.

Peter. That's the clock's fault too. The coach
starts as the clock strikes nine. If it didn't strike
I shouldn't go.

Fanny. But if it didn't strike I shouldn't have
breakfast with mamma.

Peter. I know. It'll be striking six in a minute.
Time for Vic and me to go to bed, and time for
you to go to a party. He isn't even a *fair* devil.

Fanny [with righteous indignation]. Peter ! If
you say that word again, I'll tell mamma.

Peter. I don't care ! It's true ! He'll strike
nine to-morrow, and you'll be having real tea
for breakfast, and I'll be starting for school. He
hates me !

[*He walks moodily away up the stage to the right.
    Victoria slips off her chair and runs to
    comfort him.*]

Victoria. Never mind, Peter. Perhaps you'll
get the box-seat, and the coachman will let you
hold the whip.

Peter [shaking her off]. No. If it was to go in
a train it would be different. But then I don't
believe the clock would ever strike nine at all.
He would rather stop.

[*He walks over to the window and looks out again.*]

Victoria [with a sigh]. Mamma will never let us
go in a train.

Fanny. No. I heard her say so to papa. It's too dangerous.

Victoria. I wish she would.

Fanny. She won't! She says it isn't genteel, besides being dangerous. But Emily Oldfield has been in one. She went with her papa, and they got into the very middle coach, which is the safest place. She said she wasn't a bit frightened. And Emily's mamma is *very* genteel.

Victoria. But her papa is very rich. I expect he could easily buy a train.

Fanny. But you don't have to *buy* it, silly biddy! Every one gets in. It's just like a public coach, only there are no horses, and you go along very fast. Emily said they went so fast that you could hardly see the flowers in the hedges.

Victoria [*fascinated*]. Oh, fancy!

Peter [*turning round from the window*]. There it is! The fly has come! Now, listen, he'll strike!

[*There is a whirr that always precedes a strike.*] He's clearing his throat.

[*The clock strikes six. At once the voice of Mamma is heard.*]

Mamma's Voice [*off*]. Fanny, my love. It's six o'clock. Come along. Now don't crumple your dress.

Fanny [*in quite a flutter*]. I'm coming. I think I'd better keep my skirt over my head. Vic, come and help me.   [*She gets up cautiously.*]

Oh, I've dropped my handkerchief again. It's my best one. I've got an ordinary one to blow my nose with.   [*Vic picks it up.*]

Peter, hand me my fan. It's on the table.

Mamma's Voice. Fanny, I'm waiting. Be

quick ! Peter and Victoria, run along to bed like good children. The clock's struck.

Fanny [*moving towards the door*]. I'll try and bring you an orange. I'll hide it under my pillow, and give it to you when every one's asleep.

[*She goes out walking carefully, her skirt over her head.*]

Mamma's Voice. Peter and Victoria. Bed. Quick !

Peter. Yes, mamma.

[*He walks to the clock and gazes up into its face.*]

Victoria [*following him and nervously taking his hand*]. Peter, did you really mean what you said ? That the clock was a d—dev . . . was an evil one ? [*Peter nods his head solemnly, still staring at it.*] With hoofs . . . and a t-tail ? Aren't you afraid ?

Peter [*turning round*]. No. I'm very brave. Besides, I didn't mean that exactly. I meant he was my enemy. He hates me ! I know he does ! Didn't you hear him when mamma said the other day, " I'm going to take Peter to the dentist at three o'clock ? " He went tick-tock quite fast to show he was pleased.

Victoria [*in awestruck tones*]. Peter ! How dreadful !

Peter. Yes. It is dreadful. But I've thought of something.

Victoria. Oh, what ?

Peter [*doubtfully*]. Can you keep a secret ?

Victoria. Yes, of course I can.

Peter. Papa says young ladies never do.

Victoria. But I'm not a young lady. Mamma says I never shall be one till I can play " The

Battle of Prague " with both hands, and I can't. Not nearly.   *Pray* tell me.

Maid's Voice [*sharply*]. Master Peter and Miss Victoria, come at once.   You 'eard the clock, and your ma told you to come to bed.

Peter. In a minute.   We're just putting away our books and things.

Voice [*relenting*]. Well, don't be long.

Victoria. Quick, Peter, tell me before we have to go.

Peter. He is alive, I'm sure.   [*Looking at the clock again.*]   And if he's alive, he could be made dead.

Victoria [*taken aback*]. K-killed ?

Peter. Anything that's alive can be killed, can't it ?

Victoria. Y-yes. . . . I suppose so.   [*Peter goes towards the door.*]   Peter, where are you going ?

Peter [*darkly*]. I'm going to bed.

Victoria. Then are you . . . c-coming back ?

[*Peter puts his finger to his lips and makes faces at the clock, implying that it might overhear. Victoria, now thoroughly wrought-up, takes his hand, and they go out like conspirators, Peter with his eyes on the clock up to the last moment.*

· · · · · ·

The curtain falls for a few minutes, and when it goes up again the lamp is out and the stage is in darkness.   Peter, clad in a nightshirt and nightcap such as little boys wore in 1840, enters, a lighted candle in his hand.   He walks up to the clock, and holds the candle up to see its face.   It is five minutes to twelve.   He lights two candles on the mantelpiece, and the

*stage lightens. As he is lighting the second,
Victoria enters ; she is in a nightgown, with
bare feet, and her hair in two plaits, or a
nightcap tied under her chin. She carries a
bedroom candle in her hand.*]

Victoria [*in a loud whisper*]. Peter ! I heard you
get up. Every one's asleep 'cept you and me.
I've never been downstairs in the middle of the
night before.

Peter. Haven't you ? I have.

Victoria [*putting her candle down on the table and
looking fearfully round*]. Everything looks different.
[*Suddenly.*] Look ! The rocking-chair is moving !

Peter [*trying to reassure her, but nervous himself*].
No, it isn't.

Victoria. Are you sure? Are you sure there isn't
some one in the room with us ?

Peter. No, of course there isn't.

Victoria. S-s-s !—hush ! [*Peter jumps involun-
tarily.*] The clock ! Listen ! [*After a moment's
pause, they both listen.*] It's ticking so loud.

[*The clock begins its whirr, and Victoria throws
her arms round Peter's neck with a stifled
scream.*]

Peter. Be quiet, Vic ! Some one will hear us.

[*The clock strikes twelve. Victoria keeps her head
buried on Peter's shoulder while it strikes.
Peter counts the strokes, and as the twelfth
sounds he pushes her away and walks up to
the clock.*]

[*Shaking his fist at it.*] Very well, that's the
last time. I'll give you something to strike
about !

[*He goes over to the table and takes from a work-
basket on it an enormous pair of scissors.*]

Victoria [*watching, fascinated*]. Peter! What are you going to do?

[*Peter approaches the clock, holding the scissors behind his back, his eye fixed on the clock as if mesmerizing it to stand still. Victoria watches him in dread of what he means to do. When within reach of the clock he springs forward, throws open the door, and in a moment, with great flourishing of his weapon, he cuts the cord which holds the weights. There is a loud crash as of breaking glass, the clock gives a whirr and ceases ticking, and Victoria screams loudly.*]

Peter. There! I've done for him!

Victoria. Oh, have you really? [*She approaches nearer.*]

Peter. Yes, I've killed him!

Victoria [*in an agonized scream*]. Peter! Look! Look! What's that?

[*She points with terror to the floor, where from beneath the clock there flows a stream of red liquid.*]

Peter [*stoops down to inspect it, then with awe in his voice*]. I killed him . . . but I never thought he . . . would . . . b-bleed. . . .

Victoria. Oh, nor did I! Nor did I!

[*She rushes to a chair and throws herself into it, burying her face in her hands. Her howls bring in Fanny, her hair a mass of curl-papers, in a red flannel dressing-gown and slippers.*]

Fanny [*in a scandalized whisper*]. Peter! Victoria! What *are* you doing? What will mamma say? She'll be very angry with you both for getting out of bed.

Victoria [*through her sobs, without lifting her head*]. I wish I was in bed. I'd *rather* be in bed.

Fanny. But what's the matter?

Peter [*slowly, with round eyes of horror*]. Well ... you see ... I've *murdered* some one.

Fanny [*much startled*]. Peter!

Peter. It's the clock. I've murdered it. He gave a groan and died. I wanted to kill it ... but ... I never thought it would be ... l-like that! ...

Victoria. It's like Bluebeard! Look at the floor! ... Look! ...

Peter [*Peter points out the stream, and Fanny steps forward and stoops over it to have a good look*]. What do you think they'll do to me?

Fanny [*standing up straight again*]. I shouldn't be at all surprised if papa didn't *whip* you! You're a very naughty boy and very foolish. And you too, Victoria! I don't suppose that mamma will *ever* let you go to parties like me, now. D'you know what you've done?

[*Victoria dries her eyes and sits up, gazing at Fanny. Peter is in despair. They both shake their heads.*]

That's papa's port wine that he keeps in the bottom of the clock for callers.

[*She goes over to the clock and picks up a broken bottle out of its inside.*]

You've gone and let the weights drop down among his bottles, and they're all broken, every one, and that's the wine running all over the floor and ruining the carpet.

Victoria [*getting up*]. Then it isn't ... B ... him? ...

Fanny [*sharply*]. Of course it isn't! It would be better if it was.

Peter [*looking at the clock*]. He's dead, though?

Fanny [*impatiently*]. It's a clock. It isn't alive, silly!

Peter [*triumphantly*]. Well, I've *stopped* it, anyway!

CURTAIN

ROBIN HOOD AND THE PEDLAR

By John Drinkwater

CHARACTERS

Robin Hood.
The Pedlar.
Little John.
Friar Tuck.
An Outlaw.
Another Outlaw.
Sheriff's Man.
Fairies.
The Sheriff.
The Ballad-Singer.
Marian.
Outlaws, Sheriff's Men, Country Girls.

ROBIN HOOD AND THE PEDLAR

At the edge of a wood.

Robin Hood [*sings*].
>Let life go unforbidden,
>>Straight-limbed among the green,
>
>And laughter be unchidden,
>>And gravity unseen ;
>
>They're grey men are the town men
>>With crooked legs to run,
>
>But we're the jolly brown men
>>Carousing with the sun.

>I'm brother to the beech tree,
>>I'm brother to the oak,
>
>And glad the little beasts be
>>And glad the feathered folk,
>
>And when the clouds are chiding
>>I'm happy for the rain,
>
>And when the sun goes riding
>>I'm happy then again.

[*He blows his horn and his men come from the
wood. Robin repeats a few lines of the song
and all sing together. As they are finishing,
an old Pedlar hobbles towards them, as though
suffering, and falls wearily. They tend him,
and he revives.*]

Robin. Not much comfort where you've been a guest, eh, father pedlar? Bruises, eh? And whose was the stick?

The Pedlar. Nottingham, master—do you know Nottingham?

Robin. Well, yes—we do call at Nottingham now and again. In the dark mostly, to be sure—but still, a very good place. Why?

The Pedlar. Do you know the Sheriff?

Robin. Oh—the Sheriff. So that's it.

[*All his men become mischievously interested.*]

The Pedlar. He beat me.

Robin. Yes. It's a way of his. He's been told of it before. Why did he beat you?

The Pedlar. Because I told him the truth.

Robin. That always tickles his temper. What was it?

The Pedlar. You were singing a song just now.

Robin. Well?

The Pedlar. You care for a song?

Robin. A good song is a good heart, father pedlar. But what of that?

The Pedlar. There's a man in Nottingham who makes songs. He's a clean man, and clean ringing songs he makes. A poor man, but he wants nothing but a sixpence once in a while. I was walking along Trent side, master, when it was Monday evening, and I heard a song across the water, as clear and sweet as a cornflower in a maid's white dress. I know a good song—and this was clear and sweet, and rich like harvest elms. And Tuesday I heard it again, in Nottingham streets, and it was a tall fellow singing, lean, with a friendly face. I spoke with him. He'd come into the town, he said, to sing for sixpence, and would be

back again to the fields beyond Trent. And then
a Sheriff's man took him, and they used him—I
wouldn't use a bad dog so, master. And I followed,
and I slipped into the hall. And I told the Sheriff
there that this was an ill thing and a dirty thing.
And he had me beaten and thrown out. I waited
a little, and I heard angry talk. How it was
prison for the tall fellow, and how because he sang
ballads in their streets he was judged a vagabond
and a pest and was to smart for it. And I came
away.

[*He has blazed with excitement, and now falls back
exhausted.*

*Robin and his men hear his tale with growing
indignation, until at the close there is a howl
of anger.*]

Robin. Master Sheriff shall learn this time.
We'll tease him this time, eh ?

[*There is a loud assent from all.*]

Robin. Come, the fashion of it ?

[*They form into a semicircle, as in council.
Robin, Friar Tuck, Little John, and three
or four others in the centre. The Pedlar is
given food and drink. Each decision of the
council is greeted with cheers.*]

Robin. This singing fellow must be freed.

Little John. And offered a green suit.

Robin. Aye, he shall come to us if he will.

Friar Tuck. And our friend the Sheriff shall
pay.

An Outlaw. Let him answer for it here in the
greenwood.

Another. Aye, bring him here.

Little John. And who's to fetch him ? Shall I ?

[*He makes to go.*]

Robin. Slowly, John, slowly. To free the ballad man and to fetch the Sheriff. Who is willing?

[*There is a general eagerness for the errands.*]

Robin. Then it must be by lot. A line.

[*Robin and all his men form into a straight line, Friar Tuck somewhere about the seventh place.*]

Robin. Two numbers, father pedlar.

The Pedlar. Numbers? Three; eleven.

Robin. Three for the Singer, eleven for the Sheriff.

[*Friar Tuck, unseen by Robin, rapidly moves up behind the others to the third place. The man whose place he takes is about to protest, but Friar Tuck grips his arm and puts his hand over his mouth, humorously threatening him.*]

Robin. Now.

[*They number down, Friar Tuck steps out on number three, and Robin himself on eleven.*]

Robin. Good enough numbers.

[*Little John, who is far down the line, comes up and looks at the two with disfavour.*]

Little John. And I saw two magpies twice this morning, the lying little chickens.

[*All laugh, and the line breaks up.*]

Robin [*to Friar Tuck*]. Choose your men. I go alone.

[*Friar Tuck picks three men, including the one he has displaced. A voice is heard in the distance crying a proclamation, and three of the Sheriff's men are seen approaching.*]

Robin. Quick—the trees. Come, all of you; quietly; when I say " Lawk-a-mussy-be." [*To Friar Tuck*] Off to your ballad man. Round there —they can't see you so.

[*The men go into the wood, Friar Tuck and his
company off on their journey, skirting round
trees to miss the Sheriff's men. Robin, un-
tying a ragged cloak and hood that are over
his shoulder and putting them on, conceals
himself behind a tree.*

*The Sheriff's men come in, and one cries from
a paper.*]

Whereas the notorious outlaw, Robin Hood, has
on divers occasions crossed the authority of His
Majesty's Officer, the most honourable Sheriff
of His Majesty's loyal city of Nottingham, and
whereas the said Robin Hood is unconformable to
the law of this land, now be it known that the most
honourable Sheriff of His Majesty's loyal city of
Nottingham will pay the sum of forty pounds for
the person of the said Robin Hood, or for his dead
body the sum of twenty pounds. Long live the
King!

[*Another pins up a copy of the proclamation on
the tree behind which Robin is hiding. Robin
appears, feigning a yokel simplicity.*]

Robin. Eh, forty pound. That's a main big lot
of money. But I say, Master Officer.

Sheriff's Man. Well, dirt?

Robin. Dirt—that's as mebbe. But I say,
Master Officer, what's the use of calling all that
out when there's nobody listening?

Sheriff's Man. What do you know about the
law's ways, pigskin? You come with us. The
honourable Sheriff wants a few more lads in the
stables and such.

Robin. Does he, now? Now, do you know, I
be main frightened of horses, that I be. I can't
abide 'em. But why don't you wait till folk be

about before you call out all that talk? Now,
I just happened to hear, and mebbe I could
help.

Sheriff's Man. Twice in every mile for ten miles
round Nottingham that's to be cried. And you're
a likely ragamuffin to help. Come and serve the
Sheriff. There's other jobs besides horses.

Robin. Well, do you know, Master Officer, I
can't abide the Sheriff no more than I can abide
horses.

Sheriff's Man. Careful, pumpkin, or you'll learn
more about the honourable Sheriff than you
want.

Robin. I think that Sheriff of yours, Master
Officer, is a dirty, black, snivelling, rascally toad;
of course, no offence, Master Officer.

Sheriff's Man. Seize him, the scurrilous clod.

[*The men go to take Robin, but hesitate before
a sharp rap on the tender part of their
arms.*]

Robin. Now, don't be angry, Master Officer, I
can tell you about Robin Hood.

Sheriff's Man. Nonsense. What?

Robin. Lawk-a-mussy-be!

[*He looks straight away from the greenwood at the
back, as though staring at something. The
Sheriff's Officers follow his look, whilst
Robin's men come quietly from the trees and
form up a ring behind them.*]

Robin. Now look just at that, Master Officer.

Sheriff's Man. What, crazy-brain?

Robin. No, not there, Master Officer—the other
way, there.

[*As he speaks he removes his cloak and the
Sheriff's men turn round. They are too*

dumbfounded to move, and fall on their knees in terror. They are seized.]

Robin. That fellow's robe, his hat and chain and belt.

[*They take these from the first officer and give them to Robin, who puts them on.*]

Robin. Now, that is mighty fortunate. You stay here, Master Officer, and I will go and see " the honourable Sheriff of His Majesty's loyal city of Nottingham." I want to tell him all about " the notorious outlaw, Robin Hood."

[*There is a burst of laughter as he mimics the officers. Then cheering as he goes off towards Nottingham. The Sheriff's men are bound, not roughly.*

There is an interlude to mark the passing of a night. First the outlaws gather round their fires and eat their evening meal. Then they sing.]

THE OUTLAWS' SONG

Joe the Miller he grinds the corn
And gives it us free of a Monday morn,
And we've bread as sweet as blossom of thorn.

    Chorus. Blossom of thorn, blossom of thorn,
           As sweet as blossom of thorn.

We are Hobman's friends, and to Kate says he,
Let the latch of the dairy door be free,
And Kate's as right as a girl can be.

    Chorus. As a girl can be, as a girl can be,
           As right as a girl can be.

Where mine is yours and short is tall,
The arrow of one is the arrow of all,
And there's supper for any who care to call.

    Chorus.   Who care to call, care to call,
             For any who care to call.

Little John. Now, Pedlar, a tale for your supper.

The Pedlar. I've a great stock of tales. Of battle they are, and of cities in far pagan lands, and of love, and of kings and king's men false and loyal. Shall it be a story of a king ?

    [*The crowd listens to the Pedlar tolerantly.*]

Little John. Now I shouldn't wonder, Pedlar, if you know a mighty deal about the likes of kings. [*His fellows laugh.*] Have you ever been to Court, Pedlar ? [*And again.*]

The Pedlar. Yes.

Little John. And seen the King—seen Richard the Lion Heart ?

The Pedlar. Yes.

Little John. And eaten at his table, I shouldn't wonder, eh, Pedlar ?

The Pedlar. Well, I wouldn't boast——

Little John. That's right, Pedlar—don't boast—it's a bad habit and has no friends hereabouts.

The Pedlar. But I have eaten at Lion Heart's table.

Little John. And checked his hasty tongue, perhaps ? They say there are times it goes a little wildly.

The Pedlar. Yes, I've scolded the King many's the time.

Little John. Well now, if I'm to listen to a lie, let it be a good full-chested one, that there's no

mistaking, say I. You've old bones and old brains,
Pedlar, or some of them would fare ill for this.
But go on. Spin away. What's this tale of the
King ?

The Pedlar.
There was a King, and his name was—well
He went with a great sword in his hand
And travelled away to the Holy Land,
And many and many a stout wall fell
And many and many a pagan band.

He set his storied crown aside,
He left the royal ease of his throne
And the mellow shires which were his own
To be where the banners of war blew wide
In the land of the sepulchre hewn in stone.

And men he left from Devon to Tweed
Should honour his name in kingly rule,
And some of 'em snugly said—" This fool
Leaves us the corn and goes threshing the weed,
And now is the time for treasure to breed."

But a beggar man came to the English gate,
And day by day he travelled alone
Where ruffling jacks made mock of a throne—
And a reckoning soon or a reckoning late
Is a reckoning still and a reckoning straight.

Little John. Well told, well told. But Richard
is not in England yet.
The Pedlar. Richard ? Who said I spoke of
Richard ? I said but a king—any king—any king,
Master John.
[*The outlaws fall asleep one by one; a guard*

*paces round the camp. The Pedlar sleeps
too. A troop of elves and fairies come out
of the wood, dancing, unseen by the guard.
They dance, first apart from the sleeping
forms of the outlaws, then among them, and
then they sing.*

The Fairies.

Grudge nothing to Robin, O valley and wood,
For Robin is honest is Robin Hood.

And may the lantern of Little John
Be bright as ever a lantern shone.

And may the platter of Father Tuck
Bear never a loaf but the loaves of luck.

Let kindness fall to the men who are kind,
And their fare be sweet from core to rind.

The profit o' days shall never be lean
For the merry men all of the Lincoln Green.

For an easy heart is a properer thing
Than all the treasure-chests of a king.

He has little to lose who has little to keep,
And enough for the day brings bounty of sleep.

[*One places a narrow crown of gold on the head
of the sleeping Pedlar. A cock crows and
they hurry away. For a moment there is
silence and no movement but the pacing of
the guard. Then Robin's horn is heard in
the distance. The guard wakes all, as Robin
comes running in. They crowd round him.*]

Robin. Not a doubt came against me. His honour wise-pate swallowed me as eagerly as a jack takes a gudgeon. News, your honour, great news, I cried. That plague Robin Hood, your honour, will be at such a place betimes in the morning to meet one they call Maid Marian. He will be alone, your honour, and may be taken as readily as a gravelled swift. I can lead any you will to the place, your honour. Good, cries the Sheriff, I'll be in this hunting myself. Then it's sure luck to that hunting, your honour, says I. And he bids two of his bowmen be ready. When shall we start ? In an hour, says I, but let there be more than two with us, your honour ; this Robin is cunning quarry. Well thought, says he, and calls out some four or five more. Just like that he dropped into my hand, as easily as a ripe filbert from its hood. We walked through the night—over some queer land too I brought them—it was a pretty Sheriff up to his waist in muddy water. I left them an arrow's flight back there to breathe, while I went forward to see we were not astray. I feared we might be out of the path, not knowing much of the land hereabouts [*laughing*]. Listen. [*To one of his men*] Go you to Marian, and bid her come at once and wait. [*To another*] When I say " Robin Hood is here now " drive an arrow into the ground by me. And the word for all is, " Lawk-a-mussy-be." Again and quietly. In, quickly.

[*He goes off to the Sheriff, the messenger goes to Marian, and the rest make ready to hide themselves. They notice the sleeping Pedlar for the first time, the crown still on his head. They wake him.*]

Little John. What's this?

The Pedlar. Well now, it looks like a crown.

Little John. And how do pedlars come by crowns?

The Pedlar. It's odd, isn't it?

Little John. Odd thieving, eh, Pedlar?

The Pedlar. No. Not stolen. It's odd. But I'll wear it and thank the giver.

[*He puts it on, and all go into the wood. Robin comes in still disguised, and with him the Sheriff and six soldiers, very muddy and foot-weary.*]

Robin. This is the place, your honour.

The Sheriff. And a plaguy long way and a plaguy rough way from Nottingham too.

Robin. But Robin Hood to carry back with, your honour—that's a thought makes easy travelling, eh?

The Sheriff. I'll twist him and fray his green coat.

Robin. To be sure, your honour. Now here's a place for hiding, your honour.

[*They hide behind some trees, where they can be seen by the audience.*

Marian comes in, looking inquiringly about her.]

Robin. That's the wench. Robin Hood is not a mile away now, your honour may be sure.

[*Marian walks up and down expectantly. The Sheriff becomes impatient, looking this way and that.*]

The Sheriff. Where is he? Why doesn't he come? If you've muddled this, my man, there's payment in Nottingham for fools.

Robin. Be easy, your honour. I've not muddled it, your honour. Robin Hood is here, now.

The Sheriff. Where ? What do you mean ?

[*An arrow quivers in the ground a few paces from them.*]

The Sheriff [*startled*]. What's that ? Is that from Robin Hood ?

Robin. No—it's from one of his friends. Robin Hood is near to you, Master Sheriff—be careful.

The Sheriff. Where—where ?

Robin [*throwing off his disguise*]. As I promised, Master Sheriff.

The Sheriff [*after a moment's alarm*]. Take him, and the woman too.

[*Two men seize Robin and another takes Marian roughly, not without getting his ears clapped.*]

The Sheriff. Very sly, friend Robin, very sly, aren't you ? Bring him, quickly.

Robin. But you wouldn't take me back to Nottingham ?

The Sheriff. Yes, rascal, to Nottingham, and to something worse than a beating.

Robin. You don't say so—now lawk-a-mussy-be !

[*The men come from the wood, as before. Little John is behind a tree near to the soldier who holds Marian. He steps out and takes the soldier by the ear ; the Sheriff turns at the man's cry and sees that they are trapped. For a moment he and his men are dazed ; then they take to their heels, running in different directions. Little John keeps his man while the others are pursued, caught, and brought back terrified.*]

Robin. Good. Very well contrived, eh, Master Sheriff ? Ah—and here's more luck travelling this way——

[*Friar Tuck and his men are seen approaching,
the Ballad Singer with them. Loud cheering
greets them.*]

Friar Tuck. Good, Robin boy, you've done well
and we've done no worse. Hey, lads, as bonny a
ten minutes as ever a dial marked. Up I go to the
gaol-gate in the dark and spoke through to the
keeper, a stout fellow, well-shouldered like myself.
That's the fashion of it, think I—Tuck shall keep
that gate. Evening, porter, peace be on you.
Evening, he answers, surly enough. I've a message, say I. What is it ? I'm deaf, say I, and he
opens the gate. How far is it to Zouch ? That's
as may be—surly again. You've a rough tongue,
porter. What's that to you ?—and he turns away.
Whizz—my stick on the side of his crown [*during
his narrative he feints at the Sheriff's men to illus-
trate his meaning*] and he was good to say nothing
for an hour to come. Then I slipped on his coat
and his girdle of keys. In go my three lads in a
twinkling and keep in a shadow. I spy a sour
fellow on guard. Fetch me the ballad-singing
rascal, say I, and give him the keys, and luck was
with me, for he knew where to pick. Back he
comes with our good man there right enough.
Whizz—and down goes his sourness with a growl.
Out come six or seven others, not quite quick in
their senses. Now then, I cry, and my lads and
I are about them, and Master Ballad Singer lends
a hand too. Whizz—whizz—whizz—and in the
turning of a plough team we're out into the night
and clear of Nottingham streets. In five minutes
we saw their torches flaming, but east way or west
way they didn't come our way.

[*He finishes to delighted cries from the crowd.*]

Robin. And now, Master Sheriff, for our reckoning. You shall have fair trial, Master Sheriff.

[*The outlaws sit round in a circle again. Robin, Friar Tuck, and Little John in the centre. The Sheriff and his men, including those who were first captured, are placed as for trial, guarded.*]

Robin. It is said that you are cruel, abusing the power that the King gives you. What do you say?

The Sheriff. That you are an insolent pack of knaves.

Robin. Hoity-toity. You, ballad man—what have you to say?

The Ballad Singer. I sang in the street, good songs, and I harmed nobody. And the folk liked my songs and were friendly. And he, for some black spite in him that rails against a good song, had me beaten and thrown like dirt into a mouldy cell. And a man who hates a good song is no fit man to hold a King's power.

[*There are cries of assent.*]

Robin. And you, father pedlar?

The Pedlar. A good song is a sweet thing, and I love it and love all makers of good songs. And when I saw this fellow taken like a felon for the song on his lips, I spoke my mind. And this Sheriff had me beaten and thrown out. And the King who gave this Sheriff his shift of authority would do well by any man who made good songs and by any who spoke for just dealing. And the King's power has been abused by this musty-veined jack-in-office, and I say it.

[*Cries of assent again.*]

The Sheriff. So a scurvy beggar and tatter-wits

is to put the King's Sheriff to rights ! And what's that he's got on his head ?

Little John. A plaything that he found, Master Sheriff.

The Sheriff. Stole.

Robin. Maybe—never mind that. This man is accused of cruelty and abuse of his office. Is he found guilty ?

[*Cries of "Yes, guilty," from the outlaws.*]

Robin. There are many old scores, Master Sheriff, and this shall pay for all. What is the penalty ?

The Pedlar. May that be mine to say ?

Robin. Yours ?

The Pedlar. For a whim. I can devise well in this.

Robin. What do you say ? Shall we humour him ?

All. Yes, let the Pedlar say.

The Sheriff. There shall be a blight on you all for this. You set a beggar to pronounce on the King's Sheriff ! The King's swords shall sweep you out of the land for this—setting a low thieving beggar to brag it over the honourable Sheriff of a loyal city of the King. There shall be whips and halters, I promise you.

The Pedlar. Easily, Master Sheriff, easily. This were a good time to give a civil gate to your words.

The Sheriff. What, brazen-face—you to dare to speak so to the King's Sheriff.

The Pedlar. The King's Sheriff ? No, surely. The King would keep no Sheriff to beat good honest folk and whip a man for singing.

The Sheriff. Here's fine talk for a beggar—the

King would this and the King would that indeed !
But the King's justice shall teach him.

The Pedlar. The King shall be his own justice.

[*He throws his pedlar's cloak off, and Richard
    Cœur de Lion stands before them.   All kneel
    and cheer.*]

The Sheriff [*prostrating himself*]. Your Majesty
—your Majesty——

[*His terror will allow him to get no further.*]

Richard. Get up, man. You're a knave, but
crawling won't mend it.

The Sheriff [*getting up, shaking*]. Does any one
know of your Majesty's return ?

Richard. I had a humour to come unknown
and to watch my people, common folk and my
deputies and outlawed men alike, quietly, over
their shoulders. Good amusement. Profitable
too—full of strange instruction. And a beating
thrown in. [*The Sheriff sinks at the King's feet
again.*] There, man, get up, I tell you. That shall
not count in the reckoning—I've limbs can take
more than your fellows gave—it's well for them I
remembered my part or there would have been
broken heads among them.

The Sheriff. Mercy, mercy, mercy——

Richard. You shall make sport for us. You
have betrayed a great trust ; you have mis-
used a friendly decent fellow ; you have taught
your underlings your own nasty manners ; you
have put dishonour on a good song. Very well.
Robin Hood—Friar Tuck—Little John, come here.
There are nine men. Can you settle with three
apiece ?

Little John. I'll settle with the whole fry of
them myself, your Majesty, if you'll give me leave.

Richard. No, three apiece. And for you, Sir
Sheriff, you're a coward. None of these fellows
can be asked to fight a coward. Marian girl, can
you hold a staff ?

Robin. That she can, your Majesty.

Richard. Would you beat a knave, girl ?

Marian. Readily, your Majesty.

Richard. Then beat that one.

[*Quarter-staves are brought and a great ring is
    formed. Robin, Friar Tuck, and Little John
    engage three men apiece and Marian the
    Sheriff. There is wild cheering and excite-
    ment, as one by one the Sheriff's men fall
    bruised and exhausted. The Sheriff and
    Marian are left, and all attention goes to
    them until at last Marian beats him to the
    ground amid roars of delight.*

*As the Sheriff and his men gather themselves up
    painfully :*]

Richard. You have paid, and you are par-
doned. I charge all to say nothing of this morning's work. If any tale of misdeeds reaches me
again, Master, Nottingham shall hear of Maid
Marian.

The Sheriff. No, not that——

Richard. Then look to your behaviour, Master
Sheriff. Robin—you and your men henceforth are
free men to do as you will.

Robin. Sire, we would change our life for no
man's. Let us be your Majesty's loyal subjects
here in the open world that we love.

Richard. As you will. [*The men kneel in allegi-
ance.*] I go now to London. Will you see me on
my way ?

Robin. As far as your Majesty consents.

[*He calls out a dozen of his men and they form
a bodyguard.*]

Richard. You [*giving the Ballad Singer a ring*],
singer, wear this from Richard in token of his will
that you come and go to your own moods.   And
the King will make you a good audience when the
road brings you to London.

The Ballad Singer. Sire, I will make you a song
for this, as proud a song as a good King should
have.

Richard. And a song before I go.   I'll have the
one I heard by Trent side.

[*The Ballad Singer sings, all repeating verses
after him.*]

    I ask no store of common gear
      Who never unrewarded went
    Along the twilit fields to hear
      The thrushes calling over Trent,
    Who carry in my pocket still
      A penny piece for courtesy,
    If any man would stay to fill
      A comfortable cup with me.

    I have no falcon on my wrist
      Nor any beakers made of gold,
    But lips as kind as any kissed
      Are mine to kiss, and mine to mould
    In shapes imperishably fair
      The brain's tumultuous beating throng,
    The wonder of the world I snare
      In shining nets of love and song.

[*During the song a number of country girls come
on, dancing among the singers who are seated,
and joining in the song.   The song ends.*]

Richard. Well sung, and merry days to you all.

[*The Sheriff and his men go back towards Nottingham, and the King sets out with his bodyguard
to a great shouting from all. The men and
girls sing through the chorus of the song as
they go back to the greenwood.*]

ARCHIBALD

A FARCE

By W. Graham Robertson

CHARACTERS

JULIA SINCLAIR,
JACQUELINE LEMOTHE (JACK),
MARGERY FRASER (MIDGE),
DIANA STEWART (DIOGENES),   *Pupils of Miss*
MARY HENDERSON,   *Maudesley's*
RUTH MACDONALD,   *Academy for*
BOADICEA BROWN,   *Young Ladies.*
ZENOBIA BROWN,
FÉLICITÉ.
ARCHIBALD FRASER.

ARCHIBALD

SCENE.—*Schoolroom in Miss Maudesley's Academy for Young Ladies. A door to the R. leads into the front hall, one to the L. into the interior of the house. All the girls are lounging about idly except Diana, who is inkily plodding through an exercise, and Jacqueline, who sits reading.*

Diana. Passez-moi le blotting paper, s'il vous plait. Merci.

Mary. C'est la deuxième fois que vous avez renversé le ink bottle.

Diana [*gloomily*]. Justement ma chance.

Mary. What on earth does that mean, Di ?

Diana. Just my luck. Doesn't it ?

Midge. And jolly hard luck for poor old Diogenes, stodging over impositions on the last day of the term.

Julia. Margery, vous savez très bien que c'est absolument défendu de parler Anglais dans la salle d'étude.

Midge. Oui. Je le sais et je trouve cela un

beastly shame.   Why are we all made to speak French because we are girls ?   Fancy schoolboys talking French.   Do you think my big brother would have stood it ?   Not much.

Jack [*closing her book with a bang*]. L'enfant dit vrai.   Pourquoi diable faut il que——

Chorus [*shocked*]. Jack !

Jack. What ?

Chorus. You mustn't say that.

Jack. I didn't—at least I only said it in French, and that doesn't count.   As a matter of fact I know some perfectly awful French swears.

Chorus. S-s-s-sh.

Jack. Well, you are a set of mugs.   [*Reopens her book.*]   I wish I were a boy.

Ruth. Oh, Jacqueline, and wear horrid tweedy things ?

Jack. Jolly sight better than frocks.   I've got some boys' clothes here that my cousin lent me to take home for theatricals—I wish I might wear 'em.

Mary. Do you go to-morrow, Jack ?

Jack. First thing in the morning, you bet.

Midge. I'm going to-day.   Some one's coming for me after tea.

Chorus. Not your big brother ?   Not Archibald ?

Midge. No—an aunt, I think.

Chorus [*of disappointment*]. Oh !

Julia [*unpleasantly*]. I thought that perhaps we were to be favoured with a sight of Midge's wonderful brother, of whom we hear so much.

Midge. College men haven't got time to go round girls' schools collecting their sisters.   Archibald is in immense request ;   always staying about for cricket matches and that sort of thing.

Julia. Does he play much cricket in the winter ?

Midge [*coldly*]. You may be quite sure he could if he wanted to, Julia—and I don't at all like the way in which you speak of Archibald. You should remember that he is a very remarkable man, and you are only a little girl.

Julia. Consider me crushed, Midge. And I will certainly try to meditate upon my youth and insignificance—but oh, girls, do you know that I shall soon put up my hair ?

Chorus. Oh, Julia !

Julia. These very holidays my skirts are to be lengthened.

Mary. But what will you do with all your nice short frocks ?

Julia. I shall divide them between my grandmother and an elderly aunt ; they will be delighted with them.

Diana. And you'll have lots of lovely new things. It's good to be you.

Julia. You will have new things too, Diogenes, dear, if you go on growing at that rate.

Diana [*gloomily*]. Not me. I'm a mass of tucks.

Ruth. Well, I don't mind admitting that dress makes all the difference to a girl.

Midge. My brother Archibald doesn't think so.

Chorus. Doesn't he ?

Midge. No. He says—" If a girl's pretty it doesn't *matter* what she wears, and if she isn't pretty what does it matter *what* she wears ? "

Julia. Does your brother often say things like that ?

Midge. Yes, often.

Julia. He must be a profound student of the comic papers.

Midge. He is. Archibald says that we should look at life all round.

Zenobia [*suddenly*]. Good.

Boadicea. Awfully broad-minded.

Midge. He says——

Julia. One moment, Midge. For the last half-year we have heard of nothing but your brother Archibald. We could all pass a stiff examination on his many virtues. We are intimately acquainted with his views on life, the details of his wardrobe, and the marks on his pocket-hand-kerchief; we even know what he is going to use for his moustache when it appears. I now wish to put a question to the House. Ladies, are we interested in Midge's brother Archibald?

Jack. Well, he's better than footling stories about girls.

Diana. Not exactly interested, Julia, of course, but——

Mary. But he does sound rather wonderful, doesn't he?

Zenobia [*calmly*]. I am interested in Archibald.

Boadicea. So am I.

Ruth. I am—rather.

Julia. H-m. The vote seems to be unanimous. I apologize.

Zenobia. Good.

Julia. Miss Fraser, you have the ear of the House. Toujours Archibald, I suppose?

Midge. Well, did I ever tell you how he became Light Weight Champion Boxer? Amateur, of course.

Boadicea and Zenobia. Of course.

Julia. Frequently. But that's rather a good one; I don't mind hearing that again. Go ahead.

Midge [*settling to her work*]. Well, you must know that, even at his private school, Archibald was a perfect demon with his fists. He simply laid everybody out, and——

[*Enter Félicité with a salver.*]

Julia. Qu'y a-t-il, Félicité ?

Félicité. Une dépêche, Mademoiselle.

All [*crowding round*]. A telegram—for me—for me—give it here.

Félicité [*laughing*]. Allons, allons ! C'est pour Mademoiselle Me-eedge.

Midge. For me ? [*She opens the telegram and begins to read.*] " Expect "—oh ! [*She gasps, drops the telegram and stands staring into vacancy.*]

All. What is it ? What's the matter ?

Julia [*anxiously*]. Midge dear—have you had bad news ?

Midge [*vaguely*]. Yes—No——

Jack [*picking up the telegram*]. " Expect Archibald 5.30. Auntie."

Chorus. O-o—oh !

Mary. Archibald !

Ruth. Five-thirty !

Diana [*brightening up*]. I shall put on my muslin —oh, it's packed. Just my luck.

[*Relapses into gloom.*]

Félicité. Et Mesdemoiselles sont servies. Tea is ready.

Mary. Oh, come on. Let's hurry.

Ruth. Yes, wouldn't it be dreadful if we missed him ?

Diana. I'm not going to hurry. There are always crumpets on breaking-up day.

Mary. } Come along, come along.
Ruth. }

[*Jack has thrown herself into a chair, and Midge
    still stands stricken. The other girls all make
    for the door ; as they are filing out into the
    hall they stop.*]

Mary. I say—look.

Julia. A man's coat hanging in the hall.
Midge, can we be entertaining Archibald un-
awares ?

Jack [*from her chair*]. Pooh, it's old Maudie's
new reach-me-down ; she's been to the Bargain
Basement again.

Félicité. Mais non, Mademoiselle. It is the coat
of Miss Maudesley's brother. He comes to-morrow
for les vacances—what you call ze 'olidays—and
deposed his baggage this morning.

Midge [*from force of habit, but in a miserable
    voice.*] You should see my brother Archibald's new
coat. Real sable lined and—— [*Catches sight of
the telegram on the floor.*] Oh, my goodness !

Julia [*solemnly*]. Ladies, it is not improbable
that in half an hour's time we may be face to face
with Midge's brother Archibald's new coat. Let
us fortify ourselves with tea in preparation.

Zenobia [*stumping out*]. Good.

[*The girls crowd out chattering eagerly, followed by
    Félicité. Julia is heard saying, " Et main-
    tenant, mes enfants, du calme s'il vous plaît."*]

Jack. I don't want any of their piffling tea, but
I could do with a B. and S.

Midge. What's that ?

Jack. I don't exactly know, but men in books
seem to like it.

[*Midge moves slowly to door, then hesitates.*]

Midge [*in a low voice*]. Jack.

Jack. Hallo.

Midge [*suddenly rushing to Jack and falling on her knees beside her chair*]. Oh, Jack, we've always been friends, haven't we? I like you ever so much better than Julia, or Di, or Mary, or——

Jack. My good child, I haven't twopence. No one has at the end of term.

Midge. I don't want twopence, I want s-sympathy. Oh, Jack, I *am* in the cart!

Jack. The cart?

Midge [*wildly*]. The cart—the soup—anything—everything there is to be in—I'm in it!

[*Sobs, her head in Jack's lap.*]

Jack. Here, I say. Take a pull on yourself. What's wrong anyhow?

Midge [*pointing tragically to the telegram*]. That.

Jack. That telegram? "Expect Archibald five-thirty"? What's the matter with that? The whole school is in a twitter to see him.

Midge. I know. That's the awful thing.

Jack. Good gracious, he's not so bashful as all that, is he? Why, he'll just walk in and be admired, and then you'll sail out on his arm trailing clouds of glory and—there you are!

Midge [*very solemnly*]. Jack—you haven't *seen* Archibald.

Jack. No. What d'you mean? Isn't he—exactly——?

Midge. Jack—make allowances for a sister! Mind you, I don't take back a single word, but it is possible that in telling you about Archibald I *may*—have thrown in a few little touches that—that——

Jack. You've been telling lies about him, you mean, Midge?

Midge. I—I suppose so.

Jack. Isn't he big ?

      [*Midge miserably shakes her head.*]

Jack. Isn't he Amateur Light Weight Champion, and didn't he " put " something or other hundreds of yards at Lillie Bridge ? [*Midge shakes her head.*] Then, look here, my good girl, you've been stuffing us up with the most frightful busters.

Midge. No, I haven't, Jack. Not exactly. You see, I know Archibald so well, and the dear boy is just exactly everything I described—at least, he *will* be—but you must give him *time.*

Jack. Time ?　What does he want time for ?

Midge [*in a faint voice*]. To—to grow up.

Jack [*starting up, then sitting down again with a bump*]. Grow up ?　D'you mean to say he's in short petticoats ?

Midge. No, no, Jack. Knickers ! Knickers ! —I swear it.

Jack. Well, it's a mercy it isn't long clothes.

Midge. Jack, can't you *see* ?　I *know* that he has a brilliant future before him, so I've only been a little—little——

Jack. Previous ?

Midge. Yes, that's the word I wanted—a little previous in telling you about it.

Jack. But you said he was at college.

Midge. So he is.　Dr. Winslow's College for Backward and Refractory Young Gentlemen.

Jack. Is he backward ?

Midge [*proudly*]. No, refractory.　Ever so refractory.

Jack. Come, that's something.

Midge. Yes, but it's not enough—not after all my gassing.　Jack, listen to me.　Have you really got those boys' clothes you talked about ?

Jack. Good gracious, Midge, the boy must have clothes of his own if they're only frocks.

Midge. Of course he has—but, Jack, I want *you* to be Archibald.

Jack. Me ?

Midge. Yes, you—*you* ! Get into those clothes and come and fetch me at half-past five. You can easily slip outside the front door. Oh, Jack, do. You've always wanted to be a boy, and now —here's your chance.

Jack. I—say ! It would be a bit of a lark, but —I'm not much like a young man at college, am I ?

Midge. No, but you're not so frightfully unlike one as poor dear Archie. Oh, Jack, he's so small —and he always has a cold in his head. Oh— when I think of him coming trotting in at that door——

Jack. But—look here. What are we going to do when he *does* turn up ?

Midge. We—we'll say he's somebody else—his own younger brother.

Jack. But he'll jolly well know that he isn't.

Midge. No, he won't—not if *I* tell him he *is*. I have not been his sister for eight years for nothing.

Jack. But—— [*The front door bell rings.*] What's that ?

Midge [*horrified*]. Oh it *can't* be—it isn't five yet. [*They peer out into the hall, a knock follows ring.*] No, it's the postman : there go the letters —plop into the box.

Jack. Julia will be out after them in a minute, I bet. She's always nosing round the letter-box.

Midge. It's everywhere, that nose of hers. Oh, Jack, when you're Archibald—and you *are* going to be Archibald, aren't you ? Oh, you *are*.

Jack [*grinning*]. I—suppose so.

Midge. I knew you would. Well, when you're Archibald, do, for my sake, take it out of Julia a bit.

[*Julia peeps in from the hall on hearing her name, then listens deliberately. After a few sentences she steals quietly into the room and crouches down behind the table.*]

Jack. Take it out of Julia ?

Midge. Take her down a peg. You can easily.

Jack. But why ? She's a rattling good sort, old Julia.

[*Julia kisses her hand to Jack across the table.*]

Midge. I know ; but she patronizes me so. She'd call me " child " if she dared—and she has never been nice about Archibald. She doesn't believe in him, and she shows it.

Jack. Not far wrong there, is she ?

Midge. No, but it isn't friendly. Why, I have believed the most frightful crackers of hers. D'you remember that one about the Prince of Wales and the glass of milk and soda ? Well, I tried and tried to believe that ; I tried till I ached, and at last I *did*. That's friendship.

Jack [*laughing*]. I could give her a bit of a roasting : I know a good many of her little back numbers. [*Julia shakes her fist at Jack.*]

Jack. But, I say—I ought to know something about my own family, now I am your brother. Usual allowance of parents, I suppose ?

Midge. No, only half. Mother.

Jack. Have I any other sisters ?

Midge. One older than me. Not very nice. She's called Tibbs.

Jack. Tibbs. Anybody else ?

Midge. Oh, dogs and cats and things, you know. Remember the dogs. And now run and get into your boy's clothes quick.

Jack. All right ; and then I'll nip down, let myself out, ring the bell, and—enter Archibald.

Midge. And mind, Jack, a great big ring—as if you had bought the place and were just moving in. That's how Archibald always rings. [*Jack coughs discreetly.*] I mean that's how he *will* ring —some day.

Jack. Right-o. [*At door.*] I say, by the bye, do I kiss you ?

Midge. Of *course* not—nor any one else. Remember you are a *man.*

Jack. I see. Here comes some one. Tell 'em I'm off tea. My eye, what a lark.

[*Exit Jack* L., *as Félicité enters* R.]

Félicité. Mees Jacqueline, Mees Midge—the tea goes to cool itself. Will you not come ?

Midge. Jack doesn't want any tea, and I am expecting my brother.

Félicité [*touched*]. Ah, the good little heart. You love him so much—you cannot eat for joy.

Midge [*absently*]. Did you notice if Diana had got through all the crumpets ?

Félicité. Pas encore. Not quite, I think.

Midge. Then I may as well go in. Thank you, Félicité. [*Exit* R.]

Félicité. Pas de quoi, Mademoiselle.

[*She tidies room, arranging chairs, etc.*]

Julia [*in a muffled tone from under the table*]. Félicité.

Félicité. Mais—qu'est ce que—— ? [*Julia begins to emerge still covered by the tablecloth.*] Ah—mon Dieu ! Ah. Ah. A-a-h !

Julia. S-s-sh, Félicité, don't be a fool ! [*Struggles out of the cloth.*] It's me—it's I. Don't bring them all in !

Félicité [*collapsing into a chair*]. Ah, Mademoiselle Julie—how you have made me a fright !

Julia [*coldly*]. So sorry. Shall I slap your hands or put the door key down your back ?

Félicité. Non—non—I breathe again. No—slap—no door key. All is well.

Julia. That's right. Because I want you to be very kind and to do something for me. Hanging in the hall there's a gentleman's coat.

Félicité. The coat of Miss Maudesley's brother. He deposed his baggage——

Julia. Yes, I know. Miss Midge is expecting *her* brother this afternoon.

Félicité. But yes, Mademoiselle. A cinq heures et demi—'alf-past five.

Julia. Well, when you have shown him in, Félicité, I want you to bring that coat to my room, and then—then I'll tell you what to do next.

Félicité. Mais—Mees Maudesley. She would not approve.

Julia. She would know nothing about it.

Félicité. Ah, Mademoiselle, she reposes herself on me, the good Mees. She—how do you call it ? —tr-r-ust me. And you will that I abuse her ?

Julia. I don't want you to abuse anybody. I merely ask you to do a little thing for me and you make all this fuss.

Félicité. Fuss ? Ah, there will be fuss when Mees Maudesley say to me, " Félicité, you have

deceived me. You will take——" Ah, mon Dieu
—what is it that I shall take ?

Julia. Not a month's warning, I hope ?

Félicité. C'est ça. Month's warning. No, no.
For me I am faithful—I do not such things. And
Mademoiselle—she is Massière—what you call
Head Girl—she too must be faithful. And for
the coat—non, tout court—all short, no.

Julia [*after a pause*]. Félicité—thank you.
[*Shakes hands.*] Those noble words have recalled
me to my better self. From henceforth my life
shall be as blameless as Miss Maudesley's own—
and I shall make full confession to her of all past
indiscretions. [*With a deep sigh.*] Only last
Saturday she kindly allowed me to go into the
town to match wool and to buy buttons.

Félicité [*uneasily*]. Eh bien ?

Julia. Félicité, I bought buttons and I matched
wools—but I also had a Baba au rhum at Bignon's,
and saw the last two Acts of *The Golliwog Girl.*

Félicité. Mon Dieu ! How she was dull, cette
Gollivog !

Julia. Ah, I remember, *you* were with me.
That will make things a little awkward for you,
I'm afraid, but—my conscience, Félicité.

Félicité [*sulkily*]. Oui, oui.

Julia. Then last Tuesday I smuggled a supper
of jam puffs and lemonade into the girls' bedroom.

Félicité. I—I smoggle.

Julia. At my request. You were quite, quite
free from blame—though I fear that Miss Maudesley will not take that view.

Félicité. Then why derange the good Mees ?

Julia. My conscience again, you see. You've
set it going, and—it pricks.

Félicité. Would she preeck so moch inside Monsieur Maudesley's coat ?

Julia. I fancy not. I rather think that the coat would—in a way—muffle it.

Félicité. You are clevare young lady, Mademoiselle Julie. Vous irez loin—you will go fa-ar. [*Julia sweeps a curtsey.*] I bring you that coat.

Julia. I suppose, Félicité—while you're about it, you couldn't manage to get me the—the other things as well ?

Félicité. The—other sings ?

Julia. Yes, the—er——

Félicité. Ah, pour cela non. Jamais de la vie ! Au grand jamais ! Cer-tainly not !

Julia. Well, then, I must manage with my riding gaiters. Here come the girls. You'll bring the coat and you won't say anything to anybody ?

Félicité. Pas un mot. Not one single word. Mademoiselle may trust me.

[*Exit Félicité* L. *The chatter of the girls is heard off, and soon they troop in* R.]

Mary [*glancing round*]. Not here yet. That's all right.

Zenobia [*stumping in*]. Good.

Ruth. We should have heard the bell. The postman rang just as I was drinking milk. I nearly choked.

Boadicea [*sweetly*]. I *did* choke.

Diana. No wonder. The crumpets were awfully flabby.

Midge. I'm sure they were if *you* say so, dear ; you ought to know.

Diana. Well, when people come in ten minutes late they can't expect to find much.

Midge. No, dear, I didn't.

Mary [*dreamily*]. How do you suppose he'll come ? On horseback ?

Midge. As we're going home by train, probably not—though of course he's a splendid rider.

Mary. I felt sure he was.

Diana. You'll introduce him to me, won't you ? —though I shan't know what on earth to say to him.

Ruth. Oh, I always think it's so easy to talk to gentlemen, don't you ?

Mary. I—I haven't tried very often.

Zenobia. I have.

Boadicea [*gently*]. It's not very difficult.

Julia. And am *I* to be honoured by an introduction to the Paragon ?

Midge. I shall mention your name with the others, Julia, but I'll tell you at once, that he doesn't admire tall girls.

Julia. Ah, then I shall have to fall back upon my conversational powers. I hope he won't snub me.

Midge. Archibald is always polite.

Julia. What a comfort that is, isn't it ? I feel much less nervous, Midge dear.

Midge. I do not exactly know why, Julia, but when you speak in that voice, I could slap you.

Chorus. Midge !

Midge [*firmly*]. So I could !

Julia [*smiling*]. Well, don't let us be discovered slapping when the visitor is announced.

Ruth. Oh no. Let's settle what we shall be doing when he comes in. I shall be arranging flowers. Just tip those out of the vase. Thanks.

Diana. I shall sit dreaming by the fire—oh, it's out. Just my luck.

Mary. I shall be reading quite naturally.

Diana. I say, let's see you do it. I'm sure *I* couldn't.

Mary. Why—somehow so [*giggling*]. Oh, I can't if people look at me.

Diana. I don't see what's the good of it then.

Julia. Now—are we all ready ? [*Pointing to each in turn.*] Ruth, you're artistic, I suppose.

Ruth [*clinging to her flowers*]. Yes.

Julia. You're dreamy, you're natural. Zenobia, what are you ?

Zenobia [*promptly*]. Shy.

Julia. And you, Boadicea ?

Boadicea. Oh—just nice, I think.

Julia [*blowing a kiss*]. Duck, you always are. And I, ladies, for my part——

[*A tremendous ring is heard.*]

Midge. That's Archibald.

Ruth. *What* a ring !

Mary. He must be an immensely powerful man.

Julia. Now, girls, places—places !

[*General confusion.*]

Ruth [*to Mary*]. Don't you touch my flowers. Go and read naturally.

Mary. How can I ? You're sitting on my book.

Diana [*wildly*]. Mary, I *will* have that chair—I can't dream standing up.

[*An apparently hopeless scuffle, which, as the door opens, resolves itself into a charming picture of studious and unconscious maidenhood.*]

[*Enter Félicité.*]

Félicité. Mr. Archibald Fraser.

[*Enter Jacqueline as a boy in a neat tweed suit and carrying a brown hat, gloves, and a swagger cane. Félicité, after a glance from Julia, leaves the room.*]

Midge [*coming forward*]. Archibald!

Jack [*chucking her under the chin with the cane*]. Tootle-loo, Sis. Ladies—— [*Salutes.*]

Midge. You *are* early, dear.

Jack. You bet. Drove down tandem, y'know. Passed 'em all on the road! [*Puts down hat and gloves on the table.*] Well, what's the latest from home? How's the mater?

Midge. All right. I heard this morning.

Jack. And—what's her silly name—Tubbs? No—Tibbs. How's Tibbs?

Midge. Tibbs is quite well—and, Archie, you never asked after dear old Granny.

Jack. Ah, but I was going to. How *is* the good old lady, bless her?

Midge. She's fine. She's been awfully ill, you know, but only last week she sat up again and balanced a biscuit on her nose.

Jack. Balanced *what* on her nose?

Midge. A biscuit.

Jack. Well, but—I say, you know! She ought to see somebody about it. The old girl must be clean off her chump!

Midge [*softly*]. Granny's a dog, silly. [*Hastily.*] And I must introduce you to Miss Stewart—Miss Henderson—Miss Macdonald—Miss Brown and Miss Zenobia Brown—and er—oh yes, Miss Julia Sinclair.

[*Jack shakes hands and murmurs politely to each until she arrives at Julia, whom she greets with special effusion.*]

Jack. And how do *you* do, Miss Sinclair? I've heard so much about you from—from my sister. I hope we are going to be tremendous friends.

Julia. I must look forward to another oppor-

tunity, Mr. Fraser.   Just now I am unfortunately
much occupied, so—if you will excuse me——

[*She sails out* R. *with a deep curtsey.   Jack stares
after her, then draws Midge down stage.*]

Jack [*softly*].   I say, Midge, Julia's turned nasty.
D'you think she smells a rat ?

Midge [*softly*].   She might smell anything with
that nose of hers.   But I think it's all right.   I
think she——

[*Draws Jack aside and whispers to her.   The
girls collect in a group and chatter softly.*]

Ruth.   Not very polite of him to whisper just
after he has been introduced to us.

Mary.   Isn't he rather—small ?

Diana.   And young.   Not a sign of a moustache.

Mary.   I am disappointed.

Boadicea.   Aren't *you* disappointed, Zenobia ?

Zenobia.   No, I like him.

Diana.   I think old Julia scored.   That's the
way to treat such a mere boy.

Ruth.   I shall be very cold in my manner.

Midge [*bringing Jack down*].   And now, Archie,
we mustn't talk secrets any longer.   Come and
make friends with the girls.   [*Aside.*]   Now then,
Jack—jump in.

Jack [*with an effort*].   I'm jolly glad to meet you
young ladies at last.   My sister Margy is always
talking about you.

Ruth [*frostily*].   Indeed !

Jack.   So I thought I'd just pop down and get
her to trot you out for me.

Mary [*icily*].   Most kind of you.

Diana [*sternly*].   I have not trotted for years,
Mr. Fraser.

Jack [*to Midge*].   No go, so far.

Midge. Never mind, try again.

Jack [*picking up Diana's exercise book*]. You write, I see, Miss Stewart.

Diana. Oh, not exactly *write*, you know.

Jack [*reading*]. " Procrastination is the thief of time."—But how finely put. I can't tell you how much I should value a few of these lines from your pen.

Diana. You can take the lot if you like. I don't want 'em. [*Turns her back.*]

Jack [*coming to Ruth with persevering gallantry*]. You're fond of flowers, Miss Macdonald. I'm sure you have a garden.

Ruth. A very little one.

Jack. I should like to roam round that little garden with *you*.

Ruth. It would not take you long, Mr. Fraser. It is only some mustard and cress on a flannel.

[*Turns her back.*]

Jack [*to Midge*]. Look here, Midge, I've had about enough of this. Talk of collar work !

Midge. Do go on, Jack. I'm sure they're getting interested.

Jack. Well, I'll interest 'em *this* time, you can bet. Ahem—[*to the girls*] by the bye, isn't there one of you that I haven't seen yet—a queer name —Spotty—Dotty—— ?

Mary. Lemothe ? Jack Lemothe ?

Jack. That's it. Can't I see her ? Margy here says she's the pick of the bunch. As pretty as a picture—and clever too.

Diana. Really ? She's a nice enough girl, but I shouldn't call her pretty.

Ruth. Oh yes, pretty in a very ordinary way, but certainly not clever.

Boadicea. Would *you* call her pretty, Zenobia ?

Zenobia. No.

Jack [*to Midge*]. They're warming up. The mixture as before—eh ?

Midge. Rather. Rub it in.

Jack [*loudly*]. Well, you surprise me. Tell you the truth, I came expressly to see Miss What's-her-name.

Ruth. Miss Lemothe ? Really ?

Jack. When Margy showed me her photograph, with all that lovely hair—you know—loose about her shoulders, I said :

" Was this the face that launched a thousand ships,
    And burnt the topless towers of Ilium ? "

Mary. I—I don't think it could have been.

Ruth. I never heard of anything of the sort happening.

Diana. And if she'd launched so much as a penny steamer with her face I'm sure she would have mentioned it.

Mary. Such an odd thing to do.

Jack. But I say, her smile, you know—eh ?

Ruth. Do you really think it so much nicer than —other people's, Mr. Fraser ?

[*Smiles elaborately*.]

Jack. Other people's ? Whose ?

All [*smiling industriously at Jack*]. Oh—anybody's.

Jack [*to Midge*]. Got 'em *this* time, I think. [*With a bow to the girls*.] I haven't been favoured with anybody's smiles up to this, you see, so how was I to judge ?

Ruth. But—now that you *have* ?

[*All smile their hardest*.]

Jack. Now that I *have*—I don't think we'll trouble Miss Lemothe to come down.

[*The girls all cluster round him.*]

Diana. We didn't like to be too friendly at first.

Mary. We felt that we didn't really know you yet.

Jack. Ah, but that was five minutes ago.

Mary. You're getting quite an old friend *now*.

Ruth. I almost feel as if you were *my* big brother.

Boadicea. So do I.

Jack [*to Midge*]. Feeding out of my hand, you see.

Midge [*softly*]. Jack, you're splendid. Keep it up.

Jack. Well, as we're getting so chummy—hang it all, let's celebrate! Let's have a Fox Trot to set us going.

Mary. Miss Maudesley says that nice girls don't dance Fox Trots.

Jack. And are you all nice girls?

Zenobia [*advancing*]. No.

Jack [*seizing her*]. Come on then.

[*Diana flies to the piano and thumps out a tune, Jack prances with Zenobia, Midge whirls off with Boadicea, Mary and Ruth caper together, the dance grows faster and wilder. Suddenly a loud ring is heard.*]

All [*pausing*]. What's that?

Jack [*edging up to Midge*]. Archibald, I bet.

Midge. I'd better pounce upon him in the hall.

[*She runs out.*]

Jack [*skipping back to Zenobia*]. Excuse me, Miss Brown. " On with the dance, let joy be unconfined."

[*Diana strikes up again, and the dance is begin-
        ning when Midge rushes in with a shrill
        scream.*]

Jack. Whatever is the matter ?   Who is it ?

Midge [*clinging to Jack*]. Oh, it's—it's—oh, I
don't know who it is !

[*The music breaks off as Félicité enters.*]

Félicité. Mr. Archibald Fraser.

[*Enter Julia as a man in a long Newmarket coat
        and gaiters.   She wears a white muffler and
        carries hat and stick.   She is adorned with
        a slight black moustache, and an unlighted
        cigarette is between her lips.*]

Jack [*to Midge*]. But—I say.   *That* isn't——

Midge [*hiding behind her*]. No, I tell you !   I
never saw him before in my life.

Julia [*languidly*]. Is this Maudesley's—a—Girls'
School ?

Diana. This is Miss Maudesley's Academy for
Young Ladies.

Julia. Ah.   [*Seats herself.*]   Then will one of
you little girls run and find my sist-ar, Margery
Fraser ?   Say, her broth-ar has called for her and
she is to hurry up.   [*Pauses in the act of lighting
cigarette.*]   A—suppose one can't smoke in a place
like this.   Nuisance.

[*Félicité leaves the room with a loud giggle.*]

Diana [*open-mouthed*]. Are you Margery Fraser's
brother Archibald ?

Julia. I—lay claim to that honour.

Diana. But—he's   here   already.   [*Indicating
Jack.*]   This is Mr. Fraser.

[*Midge in desperation advances to the front.*]

Julia. Ah, Margery, so there you are.

Midge [*solemnly*]. Girls, don't go near that

person. Don't look at him. Don't speak to him. He is *not* my brother!

Diana. Really, Midge, you can't expect us to limit our acquaintance *entirely* to your brothers.

Mary. Though you do seem to have a good many of them.

Midge. Idiot! Don't you understand? He pretends to be my brother and he isn't. That means he's a something or another in disguise—a burglar or a bigamist—or worse!

Mary [*clinging to Jack*]. Oh, what a mercy we've got a *man* in the house!

[*The girls crowd behind Jack, who is unwillingly pushed towards Julia.*]

Jack [*feebly*]. What—what do you want, sir?

Julia [*producing an eyeglass and staring at Jack.*] A—did I catch your name correctly—Fraser?

Midge [*taking Jack's arm*]. Yes, my brother, Archibald Fraser.

Julia. Really, sister Margery? This sudden addition to our family is a little surprising. I don't recollect having a brother.

Midge. It isn't your family, and you *know* you're not my brother. I've only got one.

Jack. And hang it, she wouldn't have *two* brothers called Archibald: even if he were twins he'd have different names.

Julia. My view exactly.

Jack. Very well then, if I'm Archibald, you're *not*.

Julia. Quite so, but you *aren't*, you see. [*The girls regard Julia with growing favour; she turns to them.*] Has my sister ever described her brother Archibald to you?

Diana. Yes. She said he was like a Greek god.

Midge [*sulkily*]. I didn't say *which* Greek god ; there are any amount of 'em.

Julia. A Greek god, I believe, is generally alluded to as the Ideal of Manly Beauty. Now [*rising and striking an attitude*]—without prejudice, my dear young ladies—which do you consider answers the better to that description, this urchin or—a—myself ?

Mary [*shyly*]. Do you know—directly you came in I said to Diana—didn't I ?

Ruth. Yes, and *I* said—didn't I ?

Boadicea. So did I.

Diana. In fact, we *all* said——

Zenobia. *I* didn't. I like this one best.

[*She takes Jack's arm, while the others cluster round Julia.*]

Diana. Of course, the question is, if dear Mr. Fraser *is* Mr. Fraser—who's the other one ?

Julia. That, dear ladies, it will be my duty to discover, and I shall deal with the matter very rigorously—but pardon me if, for the moment, I am unmanned. [*Touches her eyes gently with handkerchief.*] It is a painful thing to be disowned by one's own little sister.

Diana. Midge, I think it's *horrid* of you ! Look how he feels it, poor dear. We do sympathize, Mr. Fraser. We didn't like to be too friendly at first.

Mary. We felt that we really didn't *know* you.

Ruth. I almost feel as if *I* were your little sister.

Jack. I like that. You were feeling as if you were *my* little sister just now.

Ruth [*freezingly*]. That, as you pointed out, Mr. Fraser, was five minutes ago.

Midge. Well, we'll see what auntie says about it—she'll call for Archie and me about six. You wait till auntie comes !

Julia. Sorry to seem disobliging, but we have to catch the 5.40. Isn't that child's absurd box down yet ?

Diana.
Mary. } Yes, Mr. Fraser—it's in the hall, Mr.
Ruth. } Fraser.

Midge. He *isn't* Mr. Fraser, and he shan't touch my box ! Auntie's coming for me—I *must* wait for auntie !

Julia. Auntie will meet us at the station.

Midge. She's no aunt of yours ! Look here, if she's your aunt tell me her name.

Julia [*languidly*]. My good child, your brain is not your strong point, but you must know that.

Midge. Yes, but you don't. Tell me her name.

Julia [*at a loss*]. A—a——

Midge. There ! There ! He doesn't know his own aunt by name.

Diana. Well, you don't seem to know your own brother by sight, so perhaps that sort of thing runs in the family.

Mary. I think she might make up her mind to one or the other of them.

Ruth. At this rate we shall have the place full of her brothers before she gets suited.

Julia. Come, Margery, we've had enough of this nonsense. Get on your hat and jacket and come along. We'll give this young gentleman a lift too —as far as the police station. Impersonation with intent to defraud ; that's the charge.

Jack [*retreating*]. No—no.

Julia [*collaring Jack*]. Come along.

Jack [*wrenching herself free*]. Let me alone, I tell you. How *can* I go to the police station in trousers?

Julia. My good fellow, I assure you they're very generally worn there. You won't be at all remarkable.

Jack. No—but—— [*Bursts into tears.*] Oh—what am I to do?

Midge [*also collapsing*]. Oh, what am I to do?
        [*They sob on each other's shoulders.*]

Julia. Now then. [*Taking Midge by the hand and drawing her away.*] Let's get a move on.

Jack [*wildly*]. Oh, don't say " Move on "—it's so like the police station ! Midge, Midge !

Midge [*snatching her hand from Julia*]. I can't go—I won't—and she mustn't [*pointing to Jack*] —I mean *he* mustn't. Girls, don't let this man take us away—I tell you we don't *know* him— we've never *seen* him before. Oh, why doesn't Miss Maudesley come home—why doesn't auntie come—why doesn't *somebody* come ?

[*The door bell rings. A breathless silence until Félicité enters, her eyes round with astonishment.*]

Félicité. Mr. Archibald Fraser !

All [*hopelessly*]. Another !

[*Enter a very small and very plain boy of about eight years. He is pale, his nose is slightly red, and he wears spectacles. He gazes round the room and sniffs drearily.*]

Midge [*rushing to him*]. Archie ! Archie !
                [*Clings to him wildly.*]

Diana. She seems to be taking to this one.

Midge. Oh, Archie, this great horrid man says

he's my brother, and he's going to take us to the p-p-police station.

Archie [*with perfect calm*]. Is he ? Now then, sir, what do you mean by it ?

[*Advancing with clenched fists.*]

Julia [*retreating*]. Run along, child. Don't be silly.

Archie. Do you call yourself a gentleman ?

Julia [*retreating*]. No, of course not—that is, I mean——

Jack. By Jove. He's wilting ! [*Squaring up.*] Yes, sir. Do you call yourself a gentleman ?

Archie [*gently waving her back*]. Pardon me, sir. My affair entirely. Now, sir, take your coat off.

[*Squares up scientifically and advances upon Julia.*]

Julia [*edging behind the table*]. Don't flap your hands at me like that, you odious child ! I shall speak to Miss Maudesley the very minute she comes in.

Jack. The chap's in a blue funk ! Do it, little 'un.

Midge [*skipping with excitement*]. Cowardy, cowardy, custard—stole his mother's——

Archie. Shut up, Siskin. Take off your coat, sir.

Julia. I—I shall do nothing of the kind—in the presence of ladies.

All the Girls. Oh, but we don't mind a bit ! Do go on. It's so interesting.

Archie. Are you going to take your coat off ?

Julia. No.

Archie. Then——

[*He makes a dive for Julia, who escapes round the table. Félicité screams shrilly,* " Ah, Mademoiselle." *As Julia runs, Archie snatches at her coat, which comes half off, disclosing her frock and long hair.*]

Chorus [*of indignation and disappointment*]. Julia! O-oh, Julia!

Jack [*going into peals of laughter*]. Oh—ha—ha—ha! You *do* look funny.

Julia. Then I won't be the only one looking funny. There. How about you?

[*Pulls Jack's wig off.*]

Chorus [*as before*]. Jack!!

Jack. Julia, you *knew*?

Julia. Yes, I knew. I heard Midge planning to take me down a peg. I rather fancy I took *her* down several.

Midge. Until Archibald came along. Then you had to skip.

Julia. I skipped, I admit. Your brother is a remarkable man, Midge.

Jack [*slapping Archie on the back*]. A jolly good sort.   [*The ladies begin to collect round Archie.*]

Archie [*suddenly*]. I say—what a lot of girls. Let's hook it.

Midge [*struggling into her coat*]. It didn't take him long when once he got going, did it, girls? What do you say to Archie *now*?

Mary. We can't very well say anything to him—he hasn't been introduced to us.

Midge. Oh, I forgot! Ladies—let me present my brother ARCHIBALD.

CURTAIN

FAT KING MELON AND PRINCESS CARAWAY

A DRAMA IN FIVE SCENES

By A. P. HERBERT

CHARACTERS

Fairy Mumbo.
Fairy Gurgle.
King Melon.
Princess Caraway.
King Melon's Mother.
An Old Lady.
Richard.
Greengage.
Gallant Troops, Rough Sailors, Tiring-
  Women, and such.

(The parts of Fairy Gurgle, Richard, and the Third Troop may be doubled, or even trebled.)

Note.—The Incidental Music to this play, by Dennis Arundell, is issued separately, price 3s. 6d., by the Oxford University Press.

The play is here reprinted by kind permission of Mr. A. P. Herbert and the Oxford University Press. All applications for licence to perform it should be made direct to the Oxford University Press.

FIRST PERFORMANCE

In honour of Miss Barbara Wadsworth's Tenth Birthday, November 25, 1924.

King Melon	Barbara Wadsworth.
The Princess Caraway. . .	Crystal Herbert.
Fairy Mumbo	Jocelyn Herbert.
The King's Mother . . .	Jocelyn Herbert.
A Highwayman	Jocelyn Herbert.
Fairy Gurgle.	Lavender Herbert.

Soldiers, Sailors, Wayfarers, Tiring-Women, Servitors, Bears, etc.—Barbara Wadsworth, Crystal Herbert, Jocelyn Herbert, Lavender Herbert.

FAT KING MELON AND
PRINCESS CARAWAY

PROLOGUE

SPOKEN BY THE PRINCESS CARAWAY

OUR author, who is as kind as he is accomplished,
and is, besides, the best-dressed man in Hammersmith, took the unusual step of asking the actors
what they would prefer his play to be about.
This caused a little difference of opinion, for while
one wanted the principal scene to take place in a
Castle (with soldiers), another insisted that it must
happen in a Post Office. On the other hand, it was
agreed by all that the principal characters must
include a Very Fat Man, a Thin Woman, a Fairy,
and an Ordinary Person. All these our author
has provided, together with a Castle and soldiers,
though not, unfortunately, the Post Office ; and
he has thrown in a Highwayman as well, who
counts, we suppose, as the ordinary person. We
also stipulated that the play should be " very
comic," but, as to that, we are not so sure that
he has come up to requirements. He wishes us,
however, to make it quite clear that for the choice
of the characters at least he bears no responsibility,
though for the rest he craves your kind indulgence.

SCENE I

Fairy Mumbo's Grotto.

Fairy Mumbo, who is tall and beautiful, but un-principled, is doing a heavy sort of dance and wears a malicious expression. She is assisted in the dance by Fairy Gurgle, who is very small indeed.

FAIRY MUMBO.

Air: " Humpty Dumpty."

A fairy specialist you see ;
All mortals come consulting me,
Whether they're ill, or whether they're well—
And which is which it's hard to tell.

Mumbo Jumbo is my name.
To one and all I say the same.
Mumbo Jumbo ! Fiddle-de-dee !
Lord, what fools these mortals be !

[*The Fairy Mumbo sighs heavily. So does the Fairy Gurgle. A ring at the front door of the Grotto.*]

Fairy Mumbo. Oh dear, another ridiculous mortal in difficulties, I suppose. See who it is, Fairy Gurgle.

Fairy Gurgle [*gurgling*]. Why ?

Fairy Mumbo. Why not ?

[*Fairy Gurgle, having nothing to say to this, gurgles and goes to the front door, through*

*which an enormously fat King is trying to
squeeze his way, with great breathings and
heavings.*]

Fairy Gurgle. It's a very fat man.

Fairy Mumbo. How fat?

[*Fairy Gurgle describes large circles in the air
with her hands.*]

Fairy Mumbo. Then take away our fairy-chairs.
[*Fairy Gurgle does so and disappears.*] [*To King
Melon, who has now found a way in, and is approaching*] Good-morning. I am afraid you will
have to sit on the floor. All our chairs are at the
upholsterer's.

King Melon [*sitting down on the floor*]. Thank
you. I am King Melon, and I have come to ask
your advice. You may have noticed, Fairy
Mumbo, that I am quite unusually fat?

Fairy Mumbo [*with a start of well-bred surprise*].
Bless me, your Majesty! What an idea! But
stay—now you mention it, I do observe a certain
tendency to adiposity—nothing more, I assure
you.

The King. You are very kind. Now I am about
to pay a visit to the beautiful Princess Caraway of
Gardenia, whom I hope to make my wife.

Fairy Mumbo. I congratulate you, your Majesty.

King Melon [*holding up his hand in a deprecating
manner*]. Not yet, I beg. The Princess and I have
never met, though we have been betrothed for
many years; and I fear that when she sees me she
may no longer be as anxious to marry me as she
was ten years ago.

Fairy Mumbo [*politely*]. She is said to have
excellent taste and judgment, your Majesty.

King Melon [*bitterly*]. Exactly.   Could any woman of taste and judgment endure to marry a creature so detestably fat as me ?   Especially a Princess—for Princesses, as you must have noticed, are invariably slender.   Now what do you advise ?

Fairy Mumbo. Let me see the tongue.

[*King Melon obligingly puts out his tongue, which the Fairy examines—with a slight frown.*]

Fairy Mumbo. H'm.   [*Oracular*] You are suffering from Cotopaxia.

The King. I beg your pardon ?

Fairy Mumbo. Cotopaxia.

The King. Good Heavens !   What is that ?

Fairy Mumbo. It is an obscure and terrible disease.   [*The King starts.*]   There is only one cure for it.   [*The King leans forward anxiously.*]   You must become thin.   To do that——

The King [*eagerly*]. Yes ?

Fairy Mumbo. You must take more exercise, and drink a glass of hot water night and morning.

The King [*aghast*]. Exercise ?   Do you want to kill me ?

Fairy Mumbo. How far is it to the Palace of the Princess Caraway ?

The King. Fifty leagues.

Fairy Mumbo. And how, your Majesty, do you propose to travel *thither* ?

The King. Riding upon a horse.

Fairy Mumbo. You will leave the horse behind. You will *walk* to the Palace of the Princess Caraway.   And on the way you will pick a quarrel with every wayfarer you meet, for fighting is the most healthy form of exercise, and one of the least expensive. You will arrive at the Palace as slender as a larch. [*She strikes a silver gong.*] Fairy Gurgle, show His Majesty out.

[*Fairy Gurgle appears.*]

The King [*retiring*]. Fairy Mumbo, I can never thank you enough.

Fairy Mumbo [*curtly*]. I do not ask for thanks. Drop ten gold crowns in the box. Good-morning.

[*The Fairy Gurgle holds up a Gold Crown box, in which the King drops his offering. He then inserts himself in the doorway, and, aided by the Fairy Gurgle, who pushes behind, makes his way out. The Fairy Mumbo yawns wearily.*

A bell rings, and by another door there enters the Princess Caraway, who is, indeed, extraordinarily slender and fashionable.]

Fairy Mumbo. Good-morning.

The Princess. Good-morning. What a charming place you have! [*Gurgle provides her with a chair, and she sits down.*] I am the Princess Caraway.

Fairy Mumbo. One of the Gardenia Caraways, I think?

The Princess [*haughtily*]. *The* Gardenia Caraway.

Fairy Mumbo. And you have come to consult me about your approaching marriage with King Melon.

The Princess [*amazed*]. Fairy Mumbo! But you are a magician indeed! How did you guess?

Fairy Mumbo [*with a wise and satisfied smile*]. It is my business to know everything.

The Princess [*uncomfortably*]. The truth is, Fairy, as you may have noticed, I am so terribly *skinny*——

Fairy Mumbo [*kindly*]. Oh, come! A little anæmic, perhaps, nothing more.

The Princess [*sadly*]. You are very kind. But I have heard that King Melon is unusually robust, and I am very much afraid that, when we meet, he may not like me. Now what do you advise?

Fairy Mumbo. H'm! [*Sharply*] Pat the top of the head with the right hand. [*The Princess does so.*] Now rub the chest with the left. [*The Princess attempts this awful feat, but it ends in the usual muddle.*] H'm! You are suffering from Cotopaxia.

The Princess [*blanching*]. Oh, what is that?

Fairy Mumbo. It is an obscure and terrible disease. There is only one cure for it. You must put on flesh.

The Princess [*eagerly*]. Oh, tell me how!

Fairy Mumbo. You must take more exercise, and drink a glass of hot water night and morning.

The Princess [*horrified*]. Exercise! But whoever heard of a Princess taking exercise?

Fairy Mumbo. Dress up as a Prince, and then no one will think anything of it.

The Princess. But what sort of exercise?

Fairy Mumbo. Walking exercise. To-morrow you will walk to the Palace.

The Princess. But I have a coach-and-six!

Fairy Mumbo. Exactly. It is high time you walked.

The Princess. But it is fifty leagues!

Fairy Mumbo. Exactly. On the way you will sing songs and eat nuts, and as far as possible not think of anything. Let your mind remain perfectly empty. You will arrive at the Palace as round and plump as a water-melon. Good-morning. [*She beats the gong.*] Fairy Gurgle !

The Princess [*rising*]. Oh, Fairy, how can I ever thank you ?   [*Fairy Gurgle appears.*]

Fairy Mumbo. Ten gold crowns is the usual thing, but in special cases we accept twenty. *Good*-morning.

The Princess [*dropping her crowns into the box*]. *Good*-bye. You have done me *so* much good. Do you know, I feel fatter already ?   [*Exit.*]

Fairy Gurgle. There are six more sufferers in the waiting-room.

Fairy Mumbo [*callously*]. Let them wait ! Something tells me that I must dance.

FAIRY MUMBO.

Air : " Humpty, Dumpty."

Mumbo Jumbo !   Fiddle-de-dee !
Fairies all, be wise as me !
First invent a new disease,
Find a fool, and name your fees !

[*The two fairies execute a heartless dance.*]

CURTAIN

SCENE II

Outside the Great Gate of King Melon's Castle.

King Melon is conducting a review of his Troops, two in number, but upstanding fellows and well armed with swords and muskets. There is also a Third Troop, but so small as hardly to be noticed.

The King [who is mounted on a horse]. My gallant Army, we march immediately !

1st Troop [sulkily]. We shall march, your Majesty, but you will ride.

The King [annoyed]. Fellow, I mean what I say. On this occasion your King has determined to march at your side, and share with you the rigours of the road. This horse and I part company as soon as we have left the Castle.

2nd Troop. Hooray !

The King [with a cautious glance at the Castle]. But hush ! my mother must not know of this, for it would break her heart to know that I was walking. Why, here she comes !—*Hup !*

[*The Troops, who are standing at ease, are apparently unfamiliar with this old-fashioned military command, and remain motionless.*]

The King [again]. I say—"*Hop !*"

[*The Troops shoulder arms with marvellous precision.*]

The King. Hap !   [*The Troops slope arms.*]

The King. General salute ! Pre—sent—hip !
        [*Entry of the King's Mother.*]

[*The Troops present arms, just as the King's Mother, majestically, emerges from the Great*

Gate. The King's Mother is, naturally, very large, and quite ridiculously attached to the Fat King. The Troops sing.]

Air : " Blow thy horn, hunter."

Sing a song, soldiers,
And loudly shout Hurrah !
The King is fat,
But look at that—
It is the King's Mamma !
Come, sing a song, soldiers,
It is—*it is* the King's Mamma !

The King's Mother [*throwing a single, but contemptuous, glance at the Troops*]. My dear Melon, I wish you would not exert yourself so much. You know how bad it is for you.

The King [*dutifully*]. Yes, Mother. But I do so like giving orders. And, after all, a great deal of that exertion was done by the troops.

The King's Mother. I should think so ! [*Indulgently*] Well, my dear Melon, I hope you will find the Princess in good health. I knew her when she was *so* high ; and she was such a darling—as plump and as bonny as a red plum. And, Melon, if you *do* have to fight a battle, promise me you'll fight it on horseback, because I'm sure it's safer, and you won't get out of breath.

The King [*shamefaced*]. Of course, Mother. I have always despised the infantry.

The King's Mother [*kissing him fondly*]. Well, that is all. Get some one to carry your sword. Good-bye, my Round One.

The King. Farewell, Mother !

[*The Troops march round and round and eventu-
ally off, to a martial strain, the King bringing
up the rear. The King's Mother waves a sad
farewell with a large yellow scarf.*]

Air : " The Hathersage Cocking."

Away to the wars ! in column of fours,
We march to meet our foes,
Brave boys !
'Twere strange if they won, for we have a gun,
But they have only bows,
Brave boys !
Form fours !—to the wars !
Left !   Right !—to the fight !
We won't retreat till they advance,
Sing " Honi Soit Qui Mal Y Pense."

CURTAIN

SCENE III

Part of an impenetrable forest : the highway.

*The forest consists of enormous quantities of trees.
It is very dark, the wind whistles, and in all prob-
ability it is raining. A Highwayman lurks in a
corner of the stage. He is on horseback and wears a
mask.*

THE HIGHWAYMAN.

Air : " Hark ! hark ! the dogs do bark ! "

My—dad's—a burgular !
Though a highwayman is duller,

I ride a horse,
And so, of course,
I keep a healthy colour.
Your father may
Be all you say,
But look at his complexion ! *

The Highwayman [*soliloquizing*]. Pest ! The wind blows cold, and I am wet to the skin—But soft ! Yonder comes a pursy citizen who shall furnish me with a dry coat. [*Slapping his mare's neck*] Quiet, Bess !

[*A very Old Lady crosses the stage, accompanied by a very Small Child.*]

The Highwayman [*spurring his horse, presents his pistol and cries*]. Stand and deliver !

The Old Lady [*who is deaf, walks straight on, saying calmly, in high shrill tones*]. What does the gentleman say, Richard ? I can't hear.

Richard [*shouting*]. He says " Stand and deliver," Mother !

The Old Lady. Standard *what* ?

Richard [*shouting*]. Stand and deliver !

The Old Lady. " Very bad weather ? " Oh, to be sure—so it is. [*Patting the Highwayman's horse as she passes it*] It's a nice horse, sir. I wish I had a lump of sugar for him. Good-night, sir.

[*She passes on with Richard, and disappears.*]

The Highwayman [*is left speechless, but he says angrily*]. This is very discourteous !—Come, Bess, we will lurk again.

[*He lurks against a tree, closing his eyes.*]

* The words of this song are believed to be very old, and therefore, naturally, do not rhyme, or scan, or mean very much.

[*Enter the Princess Caraway, disguised as a man.*]

The Princess [*drooping*]. Ah, me ! I am weary. I have walked twenty leagues, and I swear I am no fatter than I was before. And I find it lonely being a man.

[*The Highwayman snores, and she starts.*]

Air: "Where are you going to, my pretty maid ?"

> Though I am dressed in masculine dress,
> I am in fact a pretty Princess.
> I see a man, and, I confess,
>   I confess, I confess,
> I rather hope that man will guess.

The Princess [*yawning ostentatiously*]. I will lie down and sleep in the wet grass.

The Highwayman [*observing her, presents his pistol*]. Your money or your life !

The Princess [*proffering a banknote*]. Can you give me change ?

The Highwayman [*nonplussed*]. That voice ! [*Accusingly*] You are the Princess Caraway !

The Princess [*starting*]. Betrayed ! But how did you unravel the secret ?

The Highwayman. I have loved you since you were *so* high. [*Simply*] There was a picture of the Royal Family in my little nursery.

The Princess. Will you swear not to betray me ?

The Highwayman. I swear it. May I kiss your hand ?

The Princess. Yes, if you kneel down.

[*The Highwayman kneels down and kisses her hand. While he is doing this King Melon enters from the right, weary and dragging his feet. He looks already a shade thinner, and he has lost his crown.*]

King Melon [*talking to himself, or rather to the audience*]. My Army has deserted me. I am worn out with marching. I have fought seventeen fights, and lost them all. And now I have lost my way. Yet, courage, Melon, you have lost flesh as well. [*Slapping and examining his lower chest, with satisfaction*] Yes, Melon, there is no doubt of it, you are not altogether the man you were. [*Noticing the other two for the first time*] Stay, what is this? Highwaymen! Conspirators! I will pick a quarrel and lose another ounce! Yield, caitiffs! [*He presents his blunderbuss.*]

The Highwayman [*coolly, rising from his knees*]. Do you challenge me to single combat?

The King. I do. I challenge you both to single combat.

The Highwayman [*grimly*]. Very well. I will fight you first.

The Princess [*confident*]. And I will fight what is left of you.

The King [*grandly*]. There is no question of "first." I will fight the two of you together [*aside*] and lose two ounces at one blow.

The Highwayman. But you cannot fight a duel with two of us at the same time.

The King [*with great scorn*]. Huh! Why, sir, have you never heard of a triangular duel?

The Highwayman [*loftily, not to be outdone*]. Of course! I have fought in dozens.

The King. Very well, then. What are your weapons?

The Highwayman [*presenting his pistol*]. Pistols!

The Princess [presenting a bow and arrow which she has just found lying about]. Bows and arrows !

The King [presenting his blunderbuss]. Blunderbusses !

[*They are standing thus—both the Princess and the Highwayman aiming at the King.*]

HIGHWAYMAN.

o

o   o

MELON.   PRINCESS.

The Highwayman. I shall say—" Are you ready —Fire ! "—Are you ready ?——

The King [lowering his blunderbuss, with which he was aiming at the Princess]. Pardon me, sir, but you should be aiming at *this* gentleman [*the Highwayman*], whose name I do not know.

The Princess. But I have no quarrel with *him*.

The Highwayman. Certainly not. My name is Orange. Blood Orange.

The Princess. My name is Pear. William Pear.

The King. Thank you. My name is Pine Apple. But you must see that I cannot shoot both of you with one blunderbuss. Besides, if Mr. Blood Orange is to take part in a duel, it seems unfair that nobody should shoot at him at all.

The Princess [reasonably]. There is something in that, Mr. Orange.

The Highwayman [warmly]. There is nothing in it, Mr. Pear.

The King [reasonably]. I shoot at Mr. Pear ; Mr. Pear shoots at Mr. Blood Orange ; and Mr. Blood Orange shoots at me. That's fair all round.

The Highwayman [*hotly*]. It's nothing of the sort. It's Socialism !

The King [*haughtily*]. You agreed to fight a triangular duel, and, as men of honour, you can scarcely now withdraw.

The Princess [*impressed*]. That's true. [*Suddenly, aiming her arrow at the Highwayman*] Are you ready, Mr. Blood Orange ?

The Highwayman [*very loudly*]. No ! ! ! I don't *like* this kind of duel, Mr. Pear.

The Princess. Be reasonable, Mr. Blood Orange. You will only be shot with a bow and arrow, but I shall be shot with a blunderbuss.

The King. After all, Mr. Blood Orange, any one who fights a duel must expect to be shot with something.

The Highwayman. I should enjoy being shot by you, Mr. Pine Apple, but I object to being shot by my own side. [*Anxiously*] But I suppose you're only pretending, Mr. Pear.

The Princess. Certainly not ! [*Firmly*] Are you ready ?

The Highwayman. If you are not careful, Mr. Pear, I shall tell Mr. Pine Apple you're a lady.

The Princess [*infuriated*]. Treachery ! For the last time—Are you ready ?   *Fire !*

[*All three discharge their pieces with a loud " Pop ! " " Ping ! " and " Bang ! " respectively. All three duellists fall prostrate to the ground—and it is seen that an arrow is sticking in the heart of the Highwayman.*

Slow music is played, and it is realized that all three are seriously wounded, if not actually dead.

The Fairy Gurgle, however, now appears, and

*after a contemptuous glance at the Highway-
man waves her wand over the King and the
Princess, who sit up, all alive. The Princess, forgetting herself, immediately produces
a small mirror and does her hair.*]

The King [*starting*]. By thunder ! A woman !

The Princess [*starting*]. Betrayed again !

The King [*politely*]. Madam, I am only a poor
husbandman——

The Princess. And I am only a poor sempstress——

The King. But shall we continue our journey
together ?

The Princess [*coyly*]. By all means !

THE PRINCESS.

Air: " All through the night."

Through the wood the night is creeping—
    Please stay with me.
I'm afraid of lions leaping
    Down from the tree.
All the wood is full of shadows,
Walking shadows, whispering shadows ;
'Course, I'm not afraid of shadows—
    But please stay with me.

[*Exeunt arm in arm—leaving the unscrupulous
Highwayman still dead.*]

CURTAIN

SCENE IV

*The scene is a harbour, and the ship seen on the
stage is just about to put to sea. The rough sailors
sing a rollicking chorus as they heave on the anchor,
and a good deal of drinking goes on.*

Air: " The Jolly Fellow."

Heave ho ! the mariner !
  Fill the flowing tankard !
Merry is the mariner,
  When the ship is anchored.
Merry is the mariner,
Merry is the mariner,
Merry is the mariner,
  When the ship is anchored.

I like the roving life
  While I'm in harbour,
But when the anchor's up
  I want to be a barber.
But when the anchor's up,
But when the anchor's up,
But when the anchor's up,
  I'd like to be a barber.

[*King Melon and the Princess stand at the gang-
    way of the ship, parting. The rough sailors
    lean over the side and listen to the following
    romantic passage.*]
The Princess [*sadly*]. Then we have come to the
parting of the ways ? Will you not take ship with
me and sail to Gardenia ?

(3,554)   8

The King [*sadly*]. No. I have promised to walk to Gardenia.

The Princess. Why ?

The King [*evasively*]. It is a vow. I am a very religious man.

The Princess [*admiringly*]. You are very brave. I am afraid that if you walk to Gardenia you will be killed, for I have noticed that whenever you meet another man you fight him.

The King [*modestly*]. Yes. I do this to make people respect my religion.

The Princess [*pensive*]. I am not a very religious woman. You must teach me.

The King. You are very beautiful. [*Deeply moved*] I should like to ask you to marry me, but unfortunately I am betrothed to another.

The Princess. I should like to marry you, but I too am plighted to another.

The King. Farewell. I am afraid we shall never meet again.

The Princess. It is very pathetic.

The King [*nobly*]. Duty, however, must always come before inclination.

The Princess. Yes. Will you lend me your handkerchief ? I think I am going to cry.

[*The King hands her a purple handkerchief, and she does cry. So do all the rough sailors.*]

DUET.

Air : " Care, thou canker of our joys ! "

The Princess.   Gladly would I wed you, dear,
                   But, alas, I am bespoken !
                   Give me, pray, some tiny token
                   For to be a souvenir.

The King. Keep this pocket-handkerchee,
    Purple silk, and rather pleasing,
    And, whene'er you fall a-sneezing,
    Think, my darling, think of me.

The King [*falling on both knees*]. Farewell, dear
sempstress! I could not love you better if you
were a Princess.

The Princess [*speaking through her tears*]. Farewell, dear Mr. Pine Apple! Though you are only
a poor husbandman, you will always be the King
of my heart.

[*She rolls up the King's purple handkerchief and
    puts it in her pocket (or somewhere). She
    then turns and enters the ship, which immedi-
    ately sails away. The Blue Peter is hauled
    up and hoisted down several times; and the
    sailors sing a sad sea-chanty.*]

Air: " Missouri."

Oh fare you well, you queen of mothers,
    Away, my rolling river!
My heart is yours, but I'm another's.
    Ah! Ah! we're bound away
      'Cross the wide Missouri.

I love you best, my pride and beauty,
    Away, my rolling river!
But what is love, compared with duty?
    Ah! Ah! we're bound away,
      'Cross the wide Missouri!

CURTAIN

SCENE V

A room in the Palace of the Princess Caraway.

The Princess is with her tiring-women, being tired. Greengage, her principal tiring-woman, is even now adjusting the last hook and eye at the back, with difficulty, for the Princess has now become enormously fat. She is circular, she bulges. At her side is a glass of hot water from which from time to time she sips.

Her tiring-women sing a fretful song—as they wrestle with the Princess's dress :

Air : " Hares on the Mountains."

Oh, what can one do with these tiresome Princesses
Who eat too much fruit and grow out of their
        dresses ?
    Singing ri-fol-de-dee, cal-al-de-lay, ri-fol-i-dee.

We make her new frocks, but we don't like to
        charge her,
For before they are finished she's two sizes larger.
    Singing ri-fol-de-dee, cal-al-de-lay, ri-fol-i-dee.

The King calls this morning. We had to be
        drastic—
We've bought her a dress which is made of elastic.
    Singing ri-fol-de-dee, cal-al-de-lay, ri-fol-i-dee.

The Princess [*doubtfully—surveying herself in the glass*]. Do you think the King will like me, Greengage ?

Greengage [*obsequious*]. Your Highness, I presume he has eyes.

The Princess [*anxiously*]. You're sure I haven't overdone it ?

Greengage. On the contrary, your Highness, if report is correct, you are still a little on the slight side to be a perfect match for King Melon.

The Princess. Oh dear ! Give me the hot water.

[*They do so ; and she sips assiduously.*]

The Princess. And now leave me, for I am bored with you.

Greengage [*curtsying*]. Your Highness is very good. [*Exit, with tiring-women.*]

[*Left to herself, the Princess tiptoes guiltily to a secret drawer, from which she takes a large and familiar purple handkerchief.*]

The Princess [*pressing the handkerchief to her lips*]. Ah, would that my dear fat husbandman were coming to see me, instead of this ridiculous King ! [*Sighing*] I will sing a sad song about Love.

Air: " Barbara Allen."

Oh, dear ! Oh, dear ! Oh, dear ! Oh, dear !
   Oh, dear ! Oh, dear ! Oh, de-ar !
Oh, dear ! Oh, dear ! Oh, dear ! Oh, dear !
   Oh, dear ! Oh, dear ! Oh, de-ar !

[*While she is again pressing the handkerchief to her lips, the door opens and Greengage announces :*
    His Majesty King Melon !
The King is now in his crown and robes, but, doubtless as a result of his recent exertions, he has become extraordinarily thin.]

The King [*bowing low*]. Your Highness !

The Princess [*curtsying*]. Your Majesty !

[MUSIC—*Stately Dance.*]

The King [*aside*]. Charming ! But how horribly fat !

The Princess [*aside*]. Goodness ! What a scarecrow !—Won't you sit down ?

[*They sit down, side by side.*]

The King [*heavily*]. Your Highness, I have come to make a formal request for your hand in marriage. [*Surveying again the monstrous form beside him ; with disgust, aside*] Pouf ! This is impossible ! To think that I was once as fat myself !

The Princess [*with her woman's intuition—aside*]. The pig ! he does not like me !

The King. But I am a kind man, and after all these years I should not wish you to feel bound to me by your plighted word, if you were not willing.

The Princess [*haughtily*]. It is evident that His Majesty no longer desires the marriage ; in which case the Princess is very ready to release him.

The King [*anxiously*]. Pray do not misunderstand me. [*At this point his features are suddenly contracted into a frightful expression of pain and apprehension—and after a moment's struggle he cries*] I am going to sneeze. Quick ! A handkerchief !

[*The Princess, after a little fumbling, nobly produces and hands to him the romantic purple handkerchief. But the King is so surprised to see this that he no longer wants to sneeze.*]

The King [*to himself—examining the handker-*

chief]. Strange ! Yes. These are the Royal Initials ! [*To the Princess—laughing*] It is a curious coincidence, your Highness, but this is mine ! Ha !—Some mistake at the laundry, I dare say.

The Princess [*startled, peers into his face, places her hands on her heart and remarks, aside*]. Gracious ! Can it be my husbandman ? [*She takes another look*] It is. And he doesn't like me any more !

[*She begins to cry, and holds out her hand for the handkerchief.*]

The King [*embarrassed, rises*]. Pardon me, your Highness, it has naturally given you pain to bring to an end our long and honourable betrothal. But, believe me, I bear you no ill-will for the decision you have made—none whatever. Consider yourself at liberty. And now I will take my leave. [*Bowing*] Your Highness, good-day !

[*He turns and walks with dignity away. At the door, however, a thought strikes him and he returns, stands by the weeping woman and holds out his hand. She stops weeping and looks up at him.*]

The King. Pardon me. I think you have my handkerchief.

The Princess [*sadly, giving it to him*]. Have you forgotten the little sempstress to whom you gave this token ?

The King [*warmly*]. On the contrary—she is ever in my thoughts !

The Princess [*brokenly—fixing her eyes on his*]. You *have* forgotten her !

The King [*starting*]. What ! Can it be ? But no ! For she was as slender as a larch, and you, Princess, if you will forgive my saying so, are not.

Alas, I shall never be happy with a fat woman again.

The Princess [*doing something to her dress*]. I don't know if it will make any difference, your Majesty, but the truth is, I have got a pillow in my bozzom.

[*And, sure enough, she extracts from her bosom a huge pillow and other padding, and immediately becomes thin again.*]

The King [*delighted and amazed, embraces her*]. My Queen!   My Caraway!

The Princess. You see, dear Melon, I wanted to be fat for your sake, but, try as I would, I could not put on flesh. So I thought I would pretend.

The King. Ha! And I have well-nigh killed myself with trying to be thin for your sake. Well, well, this will be a lesson to both of us.

The Princess. It will be a lesson to me not to consult that quack of a Fairy again.—*Oo!*

[*Enter the Fairy Mumbo.*]

THE FAIRY MUMBO [*Sententiously*].

Air: " My Lady Wind."

This lesson all around we see ;
The rabbits wish they were not wee ;
The elephants would like to be
    As tiny as the elves ;

But wishing never swelled a chest,
Don't think at all about the rest ;
Whate'er you be, to be the best,
    Be first of all yourselves.

The King. Cease this offensive moralizing, and let us have a dance ! [*Clapping his hands*] Ho, servitors !

[*The entire company pour on to the stage and execute a vigorous and attractive dance.*]

CURTAIN

WHY THE CHIMES RANG
A PLAY IN ONE ACT

By Elizabeth Apthorp McFadden

PLAYS BY THE SAME AUTHOR

Knights of the Silver Shield.

The Boy who discovered Easter.

The Product of the Mill.

The Man without a Country.

Dramatic Agents
Messrs. SAMUEL FRENCH, Ltd.

PREFACE

This little play is prentice work done in Professor George P. Baker's class, English 47, at Radcliffe College in the fall of 1908. Several years later it was staged by Professor Baker in the " 47 Workshop," his laboratory for trying out plays written in the Harvard and Radcliffe courses in dramatic technique.

I am glad to acknowledge here my indebtedness to the " Shop " and its workers for this chance of seeing the play in action. Of the various advantages which a " Workshop " performance secures to the author, none is more helpful than the mass of written criticism handed in by the audience, and representing some two or three hundred frank and widely varying views of the work in question. I am especially grateful for this constructive criticism, much of which has been of real service in the subsequent rewriting of the piece.

" Why the Chimes Rang" was again tried out the next year in seven performances by the " Workshop " company in various Boston settlements. Other groups of amateurs have given it in Arlington, Massachusetts, Los Angeles, California, and in Honolulu. These performances have proved that while its setting may seem to call for the equipment of a theatre, the play can be acceptably given in any hall or Sunday school room.

Suggestions for the simplest possible staging have been added to the present publication in an appendix which contains data on the scenery, music, lighting, costumes, and properties for the piece.

ELIZABETH APTHORP McFADDEN.

CHARACTERS

HOLGER, *a peasant boy.*
STEEN, *his younger brother.*
BERTEL, *their uncle.*
AN OLD WOMAN.
LORDS, LADIES, etc.

TIME.—Dusk of a day of long ago.
SCENE.—The interior of a wood-cutter's hut on the edge of a forest.

Why the Chimes Rang is based on a story of the same name by Raymond McDonald Alden, copyright 1908, published by the Bobbs-Merrill Company, Indianapolis, Indiana.

The author's instructions for simplified staging are given on pages 192–210.

WHY THE CHIMES RANG

The scene is laid in a peasant's hut on the edge of a forest near a cathedral town. It is a dark, low-raftered room, lit only by the glowing wood fire in the great fireplace in the wall to the right, and by a faint moonlight that steals in through the little window high in the left wall. This window commands a view of the cathedral and of the road leading down into the town. The only entrance into the hut is the front door near the window.

The furnishings are few : two substantial stools, one near the window, the other before the fire, logs piled up near the hearth, and on the chimney shelf above a few dishes, three little bowls, three spoons, and a great iron porridge pot. A wooden peg to the right of the chimney holds Steen's cap and cape, one to the left an old shawl. Near the door Holger's cap and cape hang from a third peg.

Despite its poverty the room is full of beautiful colouring as it lies half hidden in deep shadow, save where the light of the fire falls on the brown of the wood and the warmer shades of the children's garments, illuminates their faces, and gleams on their bright hair.

When the curtain is raised Steen is sitting disconsolately on the stool near the fire. He is a handsome sturdy little lad of nine or ten, dressed in rough but warm garments of a dark red. Holger, a slender boy some four years older, bends over Steen, patting him comfortingly on the shoulder.

There is petulance and revolt in the expression of the younger boy, but Holger's face is full of a blended character and spirituality that makes him beautiful. He is clad like his brother in comfortable but worn jerkin and hose of a dark leaf green. His manner to the little boy is full of affection, though occasionally he is superior after the manner of big brothers. Throughout the play two moods alternate in Holger —a certain grave, half-mystical dreaminess, and, bubbling through it, the high spirits of his natural boyish self.

Holger. Take heart, Steen, perhaps we can go next year.

Steen. Next year! Next year I'll be so old I won't want to go.

Holger. Oh, quite old folks go to the Christmas service. Come, let's watch the people going down to town.

Steen. No.

Holger. The road 'll be full, grand folk! [*He crosses to the window.*] Come watch, Steen.

Steen. No!

Holger [*looking out*]. Why, the road's all empty again!

Steen [*in a wailing tone*]. Everybody's gone!

Holger [*trying to be brave*]. They're lighting the cathedral!

Steen. I don't care!

Holger. Oh, Steen, come see—like the stars coming out!

Steen. I won't see! Mother said, way last summer, that we could go to-night, and now——

[*His voice breaks in a sob.*]

Holger. She meant it! She didn't know that

grandmother would be ill, and she and father 'ud have to go to *her*. Be fair, Steen !

Steen. They might let us go alone. " Too little ! " Bah !

Holger [*in a low, almost frightened tone*]. Steen, come here !

[*The tone, rather than the words, takes Steen quickly to Holger's side.*]

Steen. What ?

Holger [*pointing out of the window*]. Look, by the dead pine yonder, an old woman facing us, kneeling in the snow—see ? Praying !

Steen [*in an awed tone*]. She's looking at us !

Holger. She's raising her hand to us !

Steen. She's beckoning !

Holger. No, she's making the sign of the cross.

[*Both boys drop their heads devoutly.*]

Steen. Who is she, Holger ?

Holger. I don't know.

Steen [*drawing back from the window and crossing the room to the fire*]. Oh, Holger, I'm afraid !

Holger. No, no ! Look, she has turned away —she's deeper in the shadow—why, she's gone ! [*Following Steen with all his bright courage bubbling high again, and speaking in a bantering tone.*] Just some old granny going down to town, and thou afraid !

Steen [*recovering also*]. And *thou* afraid !

Holger. I was not !

Steen [*derisively*]. Oh-h-h-h !

Holger. Well, I was just a little bit afraid—lest she might frighten thee. [*Steps are heard outside the house. Both boys start and look frightened again.*] Hush—steps—coming here !

Steen [*backing from the door*]. The old woman !

Holger [*crosses the room, looks cautiously out of the window, then cries joyously*]. No—Uncle Bertel!

Bertel [*off stage*]. Hallo, there—open, Holger!

[*Steen and Holger make a dash for the door, fling it open, and Bertel enters. He is a jolly robust peasant uncle of early middle life, clad in rough grey jerkin and hose, with a dark grey cloak wrapped about him. He so radiates cheer that the room seems warmer for his presence in it. Nothing to be afraid of about him ; the children adore him.*]

Steen [*clinging to him, happily*]. Oh, Uncle, Uncle, Uncle Bertel!

Holger [*seizing Bertel on his other side*]. Uncle Bertel, welcome!

Bertel [*tousling their hair and shaking himself loose in pretended dismay*]. Help, help! Robbers! I'm beset! Gently, youngsters! [*He goes over to the fire and stands warming himself.*] Brrrrr! It's cold in the forest to-night! Well [*he faces them genially*], why am I come? Tell me that!

Steen [*exultantly*]. To take us to the Christmas service?

Holger. Uncle! How didst thou know we were not going?

Bertel. I met a fox, who said——

Holger. Oh-h!—Thou hast seen mother and father!

Bertel [*draws the stool nearer the fire and sits ; the children promptly drop on the floor beside him*]. By our Lady, yes!—and walking so fast they had only time to throw me a word from the sides of their mouths. " Go up," cried mother, " I wist my boys are deep in tears! "—and I, not wishing to see you drown in so much water——

Holger [*patting his arm*]. Dear Uncle Bertel !

Steen [*rising on his knees*]. Come, let's go quick !

Bertel. Patience, patience, young colt; plenty of time. Mother said something else.

Steen. What ?

Bertel [*his eye on the shelf above the fire*]. That I should find some warm porridge for my pains.

Holger [*springing to his feet*]. Why, of course, there *is* porridge ! [*He goes to the shelf.*] Nice and warm it is ! All ready for supper.

> [*He hands the first bowl to Bertel; Steen capers nimbly across the intervening space and seats himself on the side of the hearth, facing Bertel, his back to the audience.*]

Steen. Supper ! How could we forget supper ? Give me a *big* bowlful, Holger.

Holger [*handing Steen his porridge*]. There isn't a *big* bowlful here.

Steen [*taking the bowl and hugging it*]. Nice, kind, good supper, umh ! [*Begins to eat eagerly.*]

Holger [*suddenly looking toward the door*]. Listen !

Bertel. To what ?

Holger [*awed, hesitant*]. Some one—sobbing— at the door ! [*He goes to it, the others watching him startled. He opens the door, finds nothing, closes it and comes back.*] Nothing there !

Bertel. The wind ! Thy old tricks, Holger— always dreaming some strange thing.

Holger [*recalled by Bertel's words to something else*]. Didst thou pass an old woman on the road —near here ?

Bertel. Not a soul nearer than the town gate. [*Holger stands thinking, absorbed.*] Come, boy, eat —*eat* ! See how Steen eats !

Holger [*breaks through his abstraction and reverts to his bright self*]. Oh, Uncle Bertel—I'm too glad to eat !

Bertel [*more seriously*]. Thou art right, lad—fasting were better than feasting this day in Tralsund ! They say—do you know what they say in the town ?

Holger. What ?

Bertel. They say—that to-night in the great church—when the offerings are laid upon the altar for the Christ Child—*something will happen !*

[*Steen has finished his porridge, puts the bowl on the shelf near him, seizes his cloak and cap from the peg near the hearth and stands eager to be gone.*]

Holger. What ?

Bertel. Who can say ? All day the folk have been pouring into the town as never before. The market-place is crowded, every inn is full. No church but the cathedral could hold such a multitude. Never have I seen such excitement, such fervour !

Holger. There will be many gifts !

Bertel. The rich are bringing their treasure, gold and jewels, king's ransoms—aye, and the King comes.

[*Bertel finishes his porridge and hands the bowl to Steen.*]

Holger. The King ?

Bertel. The King himself !

Steen. Oh, and shall we see him, uncle, and the fine gifts and everything ?

Bertel. Why not ? Even the poorest may go up and give. What hast thou to offer ?

Steen [*abashed*]. I ? Nothing !

[*Puts his porridge bowl and Bertel's on the shelf, then goes restlessly to the door.*]

Holger [*breaking in with eagerness*]. Oh, I have —see, uncle ! [*Feels in his pocket and brings out two pennies.*] See !—Last week I was gathering sticks in the forest, and a fine gentleman rode past and asked the way of me. I showed him the path, and he gave me these ! [*Holds up the pennies.*]

Bertel [*rising and going to Holger, who is in the middle of the room*]. Faith, real money in the family.

[*Stoops and looks at the pennies as though they were a rare sight.*]

Steen. Oh, I thought we were going to buy cakes with those, Holger.

Holger. But it's better to give it to the Christ Child. You see, He is a little child, smaller than even you—and I think He would like a little gift— a little bright gift that would buy cakes for Him.

[*Holger goes toward the window and stands looking dreamily out at the lights of the church.*]

Bertel. Aye, to-night we must think of Him— there in His holy church.

Holger. It *is* a holy place, the church ! I feel it every time I go—it's like God's forest—the pillars like old oaks and the great windows all colours like sunsets through the trees.

Bertel. 'Tis like the forest.

Holger. And when the organ plays, that's like a storm gathering in the mountains.

Bertel. A storm ?—Aye !—" The Lord hath His way in the whirlwind and in the storm, and the clouds are the dust of His feet ! " Why should He not do a wonder as of old ? Perhaps the great miracle will come again !

Holger. Oh, which, uncle ?   There are so many in the Bible !

Steen. Yes, which ?   Would there be a whale now to swallow a priest ?

Bertel. Thou goosey !   This was no Bible miracle—it happened there, *there*, where we see the lights—hundreds of years ago. [*Bertel has followed Holger to the window, and Steen joins them. As he speaks Bertel slips his arms affectionately round both children, and the three stand looking out. At this moment something stirs in the dim shadows that shroud the corner up above the fireplace. Suddenly out of the dark the Old Woman emerges. A tall figure, if she were not so bent, wrapped in a black cloak. There is nothing grotesque or sinister in her appearance : she might have stood for a statue of old age, impressive in its pathos. As she sits on the stool near the fire she throws back the cloak, disclosing the plain straight dress of grey beneath. The light of the fire reveals her crouched, swaying back and forth praying silently, her face still shaded by the heavy hood of her cloak. The others, gazing intently out at the church, do not see her. Bertel continues speaking.*]   Surely thou hast heard of the miracle of the chimes ?

Holger. I've heard folks speak of it—but I never knew just what happened.

Steen. Oh, tell us, Uncle Bertel.

Bertel. Aye, listen then !   You see the great tower there ?   [*Both children nod emphatically.*] It goes so high into the clouds that no one can see its top !   No one even knows how high it is, for the men who built it have been dead for hundreds of years.

Steen. But what has that to do with the chimes ?

Holger. Hush, Steen, let uncle speak !

Bertel. The chimes are up at the top of the tower—and they are holy bells—miraculous bells, placed there by sainted hands—and when they rang 'twas said that angels' voices echoed through them.

Steen. Why doesn't some one ring them *now* ?

Bertel. Ah, that is not so easy !   They are said to ring on Christmas Eve when the gifts are laid on the altar for the Christ Child ; but not every offering will ring them—it must be a perfect gift. And for all these years not one thing has been laid upon the altar good enough to make the chimes ring out.

Holger. Oh, that's what the priest was talking about to mother, then.   He said it mustn't be just a fine gift for show, but something full of love for the Christ Child.

Steen. Oh, I want to hear them !

Bertel. We shall !—The very air is full of holy mystery !   The Spirit of Christ will be there in the church to-night !   [*To Holger.*]   Thy cap, boy !

[*Holger stands wrapt in thought gazing out at the cathedral.*]

Steen [*taking the cap and cloak from the peg near the door and bringing them down and piling them into Holger's arms*]. Here they are, old dreamer ! [*He turns back up toward the door in such a way that he does not see the silent figure in the corner.*] And hurry !

[*Bertel, too, turns toward his left hand and does not see the Woman.*]

Holger [*in a tone of bright happiness, roused from his dreaming*]. I'm coming !   Nothing can happen to stop us now, can it ?   [*As he says this he wheels to his right in a way that brings the chimney corner into his line of vision. He starts, bends forward staring as the others open the door, then he speaks in a tone that is little more than a gasp.]* Steen !

[The others stop and stare at him, then in the direction of his look.]

Steen. Oh ! The Old Woman !

Bertel [looking to Steen]. When did she come in ?

Steen. I didn't see her !

[Holger crosses timidly towards her. As he approaches the Old Woman turns her eyes on him and holds out her hands in pitiful appeal.]

Holger. What dost thou want, dame ?

Old Woman [in a voice that is harsh and broken]. Refuge—from the storm of the world !

Holger. Surely thou shalt rest here.

Old Woman [half rises stiffly as Holger draws nearer]. Oh, son, I am so weary and so heavy laden.

[She sways, and Holger runs forward, catching her in his arms and supporting her on the stool. The others stand watching. She sits huddled forward in a position that suggests collapse.]

Holger. She's faint ! *[He touches her hands.]* She's so cold ! Quick, Steen, build up the fire ! *[Steen goes to the fire and puts on another log ; the flames blaze up. Holger busies himself chafing the Woman's hands and covering her with the old cloak that has dropped back from her shoulders.]* She must have lost her way in the forest.

Bertel [stands watching the Woman rather suspiciously, now comes to Holger, taps him on the arm, and draws him a little apart, speaking in an undertone]. We have scant time to lose with that old beggar.

Holger. What'll I do with her?

Bertel. Leave her and come on.

Steen. And *come*—before it is to-morrow!

[*He is back by the door, his hand on the latch.*]

Holger [*turns and looks at the Old Woman and then back to Bertel*]. Oh, I—ought we to go and leave her?

Steen. Not go?

Bertel. Go, of course we'll go; she'll warm herself and march along.

Holger. But she is ill. [*Turns to Steen with new decision in his manner.*] Thou shalt go with uncle, but I—must stay with her.

Bertel. Nonsense, Holger!

Holger. No, it isn't! If we should all go now, the fire would go out and the light—and she would wake up in the cold darkness and not know where to turn for help.

Bertel. Na, by Saint Christopher! Miss a miracle to keep company with a beggar! Who held her hand before thou camest along? Send her packing and make haste, Holger.

Steen. Oh, do, Holger!

Holger. If there were some place near that we could take her.

Bertel. There isn't a place on the road—they've all gone to town long ago. Bid her fare there also!

Holger [*looks at the Old Woman, then at Bertel, then back to the Old Woman, then he shakes his head.*] Mother wouldn't treat her so—she'd be good to her.

Bertel. Think of what you'll miss! [*An expression of anguish passes over Holger's face, but he shakes his head and turns toward the Old Woman.*] Well, this is idle talk—thou and I will go, Steen.

Steen. Oh, come—let's go !

Bertel [*to Steen, but for Holger's benefit*]. Thou and I will see the King, perchance—The Christ ! Thou art stubborn, Holger ; I who am older tell thee what to do ! [*Holger shakes his head again.*] Come, Steen !   [*He opens the door and goes out.*]

Steen [*following him*]. Good-bye, Holger.

Holger. Good-bye !   [*Steen goes out and shuts the door. There is a moment's pause while Holger stands staring at the closed door, then he suddenly runs toward it.*]   Oh, wait, wait for me, uncle, I will go ! [*He opens the door, starts to go through it, then stops, turns and looks at the Woman, is drawn slowly backward by his gaze and comes in closing the door.*]   No !

Woman [*moaning*]. The path—is so—steep !

Holger [*goes to her and bends over her*]. Didst thou speak, dame ?   [*The Woman does not answer.*] Thou art like grandmother, and I know what mother would do for *her* ! [*Feeling her hands.*] Art warmer, dame ?—still cold ! The covers aren't very thick. [*He looks about the bare room, sees the old shawl hanging from the peg near the fire, takes it down and spreads it over the Woman.*]   Thou must get warm !   [*Goes to the fire and builds it higher.*]

Woman [*still wandering in her mind*]. Berries— yes, find berries.

Holger. Oh, thou art hungry ! [*He turns to the shelf, takes his own untasted bowl of porridge, brings it to her.*]   Dame, here is food !

Woman [*rousing*]. Food ! Give it to me, child ; I am dying for food !

    [*Holger gives her the porridge and sits down on the floor beside her.*]

Holger [*watching her as she devours the porridge*].

Ah, poor soul ! Why, thou wert starving ! Na, just see ! Mother says that's what makes my little brother so round and rosy, because he eats so much porridge—you like it, don't you ?

Woman. It is life itself ! [*Her voice has grown young and strong. Sinks back again as she has eaten it all.*] Bless thee, child !

[*Holger sets the empty dish aside on the hearth and turns to feel her hands.*]

Holger. Oh, thou art warm !

Woman. Aye, warm ! [*In a voice increasingly rich and sweet. At this moment there comes the distant sound of organ music. Holger straightens suddenly in a listening attitude.*] Listen—is that music ?

Holger. From the cathedral ! Aye, it must be —last summer we could hear it plain, and now with so many thousands there ! [*Leaves the Woman and stands in the centre of the room listening attentively.*] It's beginning ! [*Pause.*] Every one is there !

Woman. Why are they there ?

Holger. It's the great service ! [*He goes toward the window and stands looking out. He talks on, half to her, half to himself.*] All the world is there, the village folk, and strangers from afar, great court folk, too—aye, and the King—our King ! And he will give a gift—a King's gift ! [*She rises erectly and follows him across the room. There is the strength and poise of youth in her walk. The heavy black hood has fallen back, revealing a head covering of white linen that suggests a Sister of Charity and gives her face a look of austerity and sweetness. She is strong, maternal, beautiful. Intuitively Holger in his disappointment begins to lean upon her sympathy. The music grows a little louder and floats into the room.*] Look, dame, you can even see the windows gleam ! It is so near ! It's all beginning and—I—am not there !

[*A sob creeps into his voice.*]

Woman. Son !

Holger. Aye, dame ?

[*He turns and comes toward her; she seats herself on the stool near the window, reaches out a hand, and draws him down beside her.*]

Woman. Thou, too, wouldst go ? [*Holger, too moved by her sympathy to speak, nods silently and puts up a hand to hide the trembling of his lips. She slips her hand to his shoulder.*] Another time thou'lt go !

Holger [*fighting back his tears*]. It'll never be the same again ! To-night the Christ comes. Bertel said—" The Christ ! "

Woman. Nay, son, pray to the Christ Child; pray that He does not pass thee by !

[*She sits facing the back wall of the hut. Holger kneels before her, and drops his head in her lap. She lays her hand gently upon his hair and makes the sign of the cross above him.*

As they have been talking together, the fire on the hearth has burned itself out and the shadows in the room have crept forward and closed around them till only a faint outline of Holger and the Woman can be distinguished in the glimmer of moonlight shining through the window near by. There is a long pause, broken only by the boy's sobbing, which gradually sinks to silence. As he prays, a faint light begins to grow behind him. The smoke-grimed back wall of the hut has vanished, and in its place appears a vision of the cathedral chancel. One by one objects emerge from the darkness. The light touches the golden altar, the gleaming appointments upon it, the jewel-like tones of the stained-glass window above, and the rich carpet under foot; it shows the marble arches at the sides, and shines softly on the robe of the kneeling Priest. As the dim vision grows to clearness, so the music comes nearer and swells forth softly into the Christmas processional. Unconscious of it all, Holger looks up at the Woman, his face swept with despair.]

Holger. Oh, it's no use! I'd rather be all blind and never see than miss the vision that the Christ will send!

Woman [*gazing at the vision*]. Look, look what comes!

Holger [*staring at the Woman's face illuminated by the light from the chancel*]. Dame! [*He turns to see where the light comes from, and the vision meets his eye.*] Oh-h-h-h!

[He crouches back at the Woman's feet, held spellbound by the sight. As the music changes the Priest rises slowly to his feet, faces the congregation, and makes a gesture of approach. The voices of the choir join the music, and from the left side of the chancel people begin to enter carrying their gifts.

An imperious-looking man, richly dressed in black and gold, comes first, bearing a heavy box. He approaches the altar, kneels and puts the chest in the Priest's hands, and, that the full value of his gift may be publicly recognized, he throws back the lid, heaping up the gold

coin with which the box is filled. *The Priest
turns, goes up the steps to the altar, and raises
the chest as high as its weight will permit.
The man, still kneeling, awaits the chimes
with superb self-confidence. The bells do not
ring. Slowly the Priest lowers the gold to the
altar, turns, raises his hand in blessing and
dismissal. The rich man rises, looking bewildered at his failure, crosses to the right
and stands near the altar as the pageant
moves on.*

*The Priest turns to the next comer, a Courtier
brave in green and gold, who enters with an
air of great elegance, bearing daintily a gilded
jewel casket. He kneels and lays it in the
Priest's hands. The latter turns to go, but the
Courtier detains him a second, raises the lid of
the box and holds up string after string of rich
gems. The Priest carries the jewels to the altar
and offers them. The bells do not ring. The
Priest dismisses the Courtier, and the young
man rises, turns back with assumed lightness
of manner, and stands at the left of the chancel,
watching with great interest.*

*A beautiful Woman clad in flame-coloured velvet
sweeps proudly up to the steps of the altar,
kneels, takes from her neck a long strand of
pearls, and offers it to the Priest. The Priest
receives the necklace, ascends to the altar,
and offers the jewels. The Woman, smiling,
listens tensely for the chimes. They do not
ring. The smile fades as the Priest turns and
blesses her. She rises, trying to hide her
chagrin in a look of great hauteur, crosses to
the right, and stands near the man in black*

and gold, with whom she exchanges disdain-
ful smiles over the next arrival.

*An old white-haired man clad in a scholar's robes
totters on, bearing with difficulty a large
vellum-bound book. The Priest takes a step
forward to relieve the Old Man of his burden,
and as he goes up the altar steps the Sage
sinks exhausted to his knees, listening with
straining senses for the bells. They do not
ring. The Priest blesses the Old Man and
helps him to rise. He turns back and stands
near the Courtier at the left.*

*A lovely young girl enters, dressed in pale green
satin, her arms filled with a sheaf of white
lilies. The very way she carries them and
bends her head to catch their fragrance shows
that to her they are the most beautiful things
in the world. Kneeling, she gives them into
the hands of the Priest, and, as he offers them,
she listens with childish confidence for the
ringing of the bells. Still there is no sound
save the organ music and the singing of the
choir, subdued almost to a breath as the gifts
are offered. Abashed as the Priest blesses
and dismisses her, the young girl steps back
and stands near the old Sage.*

*There is a stir in the chancel, even the Priest
turning to watch. The King enters. He is
a man of forty, with tall distinguished figure
and a proud face. His purple robes, richly
jewelled, trail far behind him, and on his head
he wears his crown. Every one leans forward
watching with the greatest tension. The King,
exalted with his mood of self-sacrifice, kneels,
removes his crown, and lays it in the hands of*

the Priest. Holger, crouching in the shadow, quivers with anticipation. Again the pantomime of hope and failure. The Priest turns back to the King and raises his arm in the customary gesture. The King starts to rise, then suddenly, as though overcome at this spiritual defeat, sinks again to his knees before the altar and buries his face in his hands, praying. The Priest stands with arms crossed upon his breast, regarding him sorrowfully.]

Holger [*overwhelmed with disappointment, softly to the Woman*]. Perhaps there are no chimes; perhaps the Christ hears us not!

Woman. Have faith—have faith in God.

Holger. I would that I could give my pennies to the Child.

[*The King rises from his prayer and goes sadly to the right, standing near the lady in red.*]

Woman [*in a low ringing voice that thrills like the call of a trumpet*]. Go up, my son—fear not. The Christ Child waits for all!

[*Holger, breathless with the adventure, rises and goes timidly forward out of the gloom of the hut into the splendour of the chancel, looking very small and poorly dressed beside all the great ones. He holds out his pennies to the Priest, who bends and takes them with a tender little smile, and Holger, crossing himself, too abashed to stand and wait, shrinks back into the darkness and the sheltering arms of the Woman.*

The Priest goes up the steps of the altar and holds the pennies high above his head in consecrating gesture, and as he does so the organ music breaks off with an amazed suddenness,

*for from above there comes the far triumphant
ringing of the chimes, mingled with ethereal
voices singing The Alleluia.*

*A wave of awe sweeps over every one in the chancel,
and as the Priest wheels and gestures them to
their knees, they prostrate themselves quickly.
Holger, too, kneels awestruck, but the Woman
rises to her full height and stands watching.
From this time on she withdraws gradually
into the deeper shadows of the hut and is seen
no more.*

*As they all kneel the Angel enters from the right,
ascends the steps of the altar, and stands beside the huddled figure of the Priest. As she
stands there, a single pencil of light shines
down upon her from above, a ray of light so
brilliant that everything around seems dull in
comparison, and while she gives her message,
the light above grows till it floods her hair and
garments with a miraculous radiance. The
Angel smiles at Holger and chants in a lovely
voice.]*

Angel. Verily, verily, I say unto you, it is not
gold nor silver nor rich pearls, but love and self-
sacrifice, that please the Lord. The Christ Child
was hungered and you gave Him meat—a stranger
and you took Him in.

Holger [*in an awed tone*]. But I—I have not seen
the Christ Child.

Angel. Inasmuch as you have done it unto one
of the least of these His brethren, you have done
it unto Him !

[*The Angel stands with one hand uplifted, as the
music rises in a great crescendo of triumph.
Holger, quite overcome, drops his face in his*

hands, and as the climax of the singing is reached, the whole tableau is held for a moment, then blotted out in darkness.

There is a pause, then the light on the hearth flares up, revealing the boy alone, still on his knees, looking up bewildered at the back wall of the hut, where the vision had been. Swiftly he rises to his feet and turns to face the Woman.]

Holger. Dame—dame! The chimes—the star —did you see? [*She is gone; he stares about him looking for her.*] Gone! Gone! [*The music still rings softly.*] But the chimes! [*He turns, runs to the window, and flings open the casement. A soft light, half moonlight, half something more luminous, pours in upon him. He speaks in a tone of infinite happiness, looking upward.*] The stars! —God's chimes!

THE CURTAIN FALLS SLOWLY

ROBIN HOOD AND FRIAR TUCK

A FOLK-PLAY

CHARACTERS

ROBIN HOOD.
LITTLE JOHN.
FRIAR TUCK.
ROBIN'S MEN.
THE FRIAR'S MEN.

SCENE.—A glade in the greenwood, beside a stream.

(On the stage it is an imaginary stream; or perhaps a strip of pale blue-green cloth; or a row of rushes suggesting that the stream runs behind them.)

All the stage directions have been added by the Editor.

ROBIN HOOD AND FRIAR TUCK

[*Enter Robin Hood and his merry men, clad in
Kendal green and armed with bow and quarter-
staff. Perhaps they are singing a verse of a
folk-song as they come. They are all very
jolly and friendly together. When they have
all gathered in the little glade and finished
their song, Robin Hood steps forward, turns,
and speaks to them.*]

Robin. Now hearken ye, my merry men all,
Hearken what I shall say ;
Of an adventure I shall you tell,
The which befell this other day.

[*As the story proceeds the outlaws show increasing
interest.*]

As I went by the highway
With a stout friar I met,
And a quarter-staff in his hand.
Lightly to me he leapt,
And still he bade me stand.
There were stripes two or three,
But I cannot tell who had the worse,
But well I wot the rascal leapt on me,
And from me he took my purse.

[*Cries of anger.*]

Is there any of my merry men all
That to that friar will go
And bring him to me forthwith,

Whether he will or no ?

[*Three or four outlaws come forward, but Little
    John drags and hustles them all back, and
    then turns to Robin.*]

Little John. Yes, master, I make avow,
To that friar will I go
And bring him forthwith to you,
Whether he will or no.

[*The outlaws cluster round him, cheering and
    laughing. He shakes them off good-hum-
    ouredly and strides away.*

*Exeunt Robin Hood and the other outlaws,
    singing as they go.*

*Their voices have hardly died away when Friar
    Tuck enters, a stout jolly man, with his hood
    thrown back, carrying a quarter-staff. He
    speaks to the audience.*]

Friar Tuck. Now am I not a jolly friar ?
For I can shoot both far and near,
And handle the sword and buckler,
And this quarter-staff also.
If I meet with a gentleman or yeoman
I am not afraid to look him upon,
Nor boldly with him to carp ;
If he speak any words to me
He shall have stripes two or three
That shall make his body smart.
But, masters, to show you the matter
Wherefore and why I am come hither,
In faith, I will not spare :
I am come to seek a good yeoman,
In Barnësdale is his habitation,
His name is Robin Hood.

Carp, Talk.

And if that he be a better man than I
His servant will I be, and serve him truly ;
But if that I be a better man than he.
By my truth, my knave shall he be
And lead my dogs all three.

> [*Robin Hood steals in, leaps upon the Friar, and
> seizes him by the throat.*]

Robin Hood. Yield thee, Friar, in thy long coat !

Friar Tuck [*struggling and gasping*]. I beshrew
thy heart, knave, thou hurtest my throat.

> [*Robin Hood gives him a final shake and releases
> him.*]

Robin Hood. I trow, Friar, thou beginnest to
dote !

Who made thee so malapert and so bold
To come into this forest here
Among my fallow-deer ?

Friar Tuck. Go and be hanged, thou ragged
knave !

Ere that I give thee one on the ear,
Though I be but a poor friar.
To seek Robin Hood I am come here,
To him my heart to speak.

Robin Hood. Thou wretched Friar, what would-
est thou with him ?

He never loved friar nor none of friar's kin.

Friar Tuck. Avaunt, ragged knave !
Or ye shall have one on the skin !

Robin Hood. Of all men in the morning thou
art the worst ;

To meet with thee I have no list,
For he that meeteth a friar or a fox in the morning,

Knave, Boy, servant.　　　　　*Beshrew*, Curse.
Malapert, Impudent.
Fallow-deer, Small deer with pale brown or reddish coats.

To speed ill that day he standeth in jeopardy :
Therefore I had liever meet with the devil—
Friar, I tell thee as I think—
Than meet with a friar or a fox
In the morning, ere I drink.

> *Friar Tuck.* Avaunt, thou ragged knave ! this is but a mock ;
> If thou make many words, thou shalt have a knock.

> *Robin Hood.* Hark, Friar, what I say here :
Over this water thou shalt me bear ;
The bridge is borne away.

> [*Friar Tuck looks at the stream, and then at Robin, with a twinkle in his eye.*]

> *Friar Tuck.* To say nay I will not ;
To let thee of thine oath were great pity and sin ;
But up on a friar's back, and have even in !

> *Robin Hood.* Nay, have over !

> [*He climbs on to the Friar's back. The Friar wades into the stream.*]

> *Friar Tuck* [*coming to a halt in the middle of the stream*]. Now am I, Friar, within, and thou, Robin, without,
To lay thee here I have no great doubt.

> [*He throws Robin into the stream, and quickly splashes ashore.*]

Now am I, Friar, without, and thou, Robin, within !

Lie there, knave ! Choose whether thou wilt sink or swim.

> *Robin Hood* [*struggling to his feet and shaking water out of his clothes*]. Why, thou dirty Friar, what hast thou done ?

Let thee . . . oath, To prevent thee from keeping thine oath.

Friar Tuck. Marry, set a knave over the shoon !
Robin Hood. Therefore thou shalt abye !
[*He climbs ashore and brandishes his quarter-staff.*]
Friar Tuck. Why, wilt thou fight a pluck ?
Robin Hood. And may I have good luck !
Friar Tuck [*flourishing his staff*]. Then have a
  stroke for Friar Tuck !
[*They fall to, and find themselves equally matched. Presently Robin steps back and lowers his staff.*]
Robin Hood. Hold thy hand, Friar, and hear me speak !
  Friar Tuck. Say on, ragged knave.
Meseemeth ye begin to sweat.
  Robin Hood. In this forest I have a hound,
I will not give him for an hundred pound ;
Give me leave my horn to blow,
That my hound may know.
  Friar Tuck. Blow on, ragged knave, without
  any doubt,
Until both thine eyes start out.
[*Robin blows his horn, and his men come running in. The Friar, not at all disconcerted, surveys them with humorous scorn.*]
  Friar Tuck. Here be a sort of ragged knaves
  come in,
Clothed all in Kendal green,
And to thee they take their way now.
  Robin Hood. Peradventure they do so.
  Friar Tuck. I gave thee leave to blow at thy
  will,
Now give me leave to whistle my fill.

Abye, Be punished.   *Pluck*, Bout.   *Sort*, Company.

Robin Hood. Whistle, Friar,—evil may thou
fare !—
Until both thine eyes stare.

> [*The Friar blows a long blast on a whistle. His
> men come running in from the opposite
> direction.*]

Friar Tuck. Bring forth the clubs and staves
And down with these ragged knaves !

> [*There is a battle royal. The Friar's men are
> defeated. A few of them run away. The rest
> are on the ground with outlaws sitting on
> them. The Friar is struggling in the grasp
> of three of Robin's men.*]

Robin Hood. How sayest thou, Friar ? Wilt
thou be my man,
To do me the best service thou can ?

> [*The Friar stops struggling, and the outlaws
> release him. At a sign from Robin the
> Friar's men are released also.*]

Thou shalt have both gold and fee
If thou wilt our chaplain be,
To live with us under the greenwood tree.

> [*He holds out his hand to the Friar, who shakes it
> heartily, and then turns on his men.*]

Friar Tuck. Go home, ye knaves, and lay crabs
in the fire !
For Robin and I will dance in the mire,
For very pure joy !

> [*He seizes Robin, and they dance together to a
> folk-song, which the others sing in chorus.
> After a verse or two all join in the dance, and
> they are still dancing and singing lustily as
> the curtain falls.*]

Crabs, Crab-apples.

ST. GEORGE AND THE DRAGON

A CHRISTMAS MUMMING PLAY

CHARACTERS

The Fool.
Father Christmas.
The Turkish Knight.
The King of Egypt.
St. George.
The Dragon.
The Doctor.

Several old versions have been combined to make the version of the play which is printed here. Nearly all the stage directions have been added by the Editor.

ST. GEORGE AND THE DRAGON

*[Enter a Fool, before the curtain, to speak the
    Prologue.   He bows to the audience.]*

The Fool.

You gentle lords and ladies,
    Of high and low, I say,
We all desire your favour
    For to see our pleasant play.

Our play it is the best, kind sirs,
    That you would like to know ;
And we will do our best, sirs,
    And think it well bestowed.

Though some of us be little
    And some of a middle sort,
We all desire your favour
    To see our pleasant sport.

You must not look on our actions,
    Our wits they are all to seek,
So I pray take no exceptions
    At what we are a-going to speak.

*[He bows again, flourishes his bauble, and dances
    off.*
*The curtain rises, revealing an empty stage
    hung with curtains.   Enter Father Christ-*

*mas. He comes to the front of the stage
and speaks to the audience.*]

Father Christmas. Here come I, old **Father**
Christmas,

Welcome, or welcome not,

I hope old Father Christmas

Will never be forgot.

I am not come here for to laugh or to jeer,

But for a pocketful of money and a skinful of beer ;

To show some sport and pastime,

Gentlemen and Ladies in the Christmas-time.

If you will not believe what I do say,

Come in the Turkish Knight—clear the way.

[*He withdraws to the back of the stage.   Enter the
Turkish Knight, flourishing his scimitar.*]

Turkish Knight. Open your doors and let me in,

I hope your favours I shall win ;

Whether I rise, or whether I fall,

I'll do my best to please you all.

St. George is here, and swears he will come in,

And if he does, I know he'll pierce my skin.

If you will not believe what I do say,

Come in the King of Egypt—clear the way.

[*He stands beside Father Christmas.   Enter the
King of Egypt.*]

King of Egypt. Here I, the King of Egypt, boldly
do appear.

St. George, St. George, walk in, my son and heir.

Walk in, my son, St. George, and boldly act thy
part,

That all the people here may see thy wondrous art.

[*He stands on the other side of Father Christmas.
Enter St. George, armed with sword and red
cross shield, and riding a hobby-horse—a
restive steed.*]

St. George. Here come I, St. George, from Britain
    did I spring,
I'll fight the Dragon bold, my wonders to begin.
I'll clip his wings, he shall not fly ;
I'll cut him down, or else I die.

    [*Loud and fearsome roars are heard. St. George's
        steed plunges wildly, careers round the stage,
        and is reined in facing the entrance. Enter
        the Dragon, still roaring.*]

Dragon. Who's he that seeks the Dragon's blood,
And calls so angry, and so loud ?
That English dog, will he before me stand ?
I'll cut him down with my courageous hand.
With my long teeth, and scurvy jaw,
Of such I'd break up half a score,
And stay my stomach till I'd more.

    [*A terrible fight between St. George and the Dragon
        ensues. Presently the Dragon falls with a
        last hideous roar and dies. Father Christmas
        comes forward and surveys the corpse.*]

Father Christmas. Is there a doctor to be found
All ready, near at hand,
To cure a deep and deadly wound,
And make the champion stand ?

    [*Enter the Doctor, carrying a large bottle of
        physic.*]

Doctor. Ah ! yes, there is a doctor to be found,
All ready, near at hand,
To cure a deep and deadly wound,
And make the champion stand.

    Father Christmas. What can you cure ?

    Doctor. All sorts of diseases,
Whatever you pleases,
The phthisic, the palsy, and the gout ;
Whatever disorder, I'll soon pull him out.

Father Christmas. What is your fee ?

Doctor. Fifteen pounds, it is my fee,

The money to lay down ;

But as 'tis such a rogue as he,

I'll cure him for ten pound.

I have a little bottle of Elicumpane,

Here, Jack, take a little of my flip-flop,

[*He opens the Dragon's jaws and pours in some of his physic.*]

Pour it down thy tip-top,

Rise up and fight again.

[*With a plunge and a roar the Dragon comes to life and springs up. The Doctor flees in terror. St. George flourishes his sword and the fight begins again. The Dragon is killed. St. George dismounts, and gives his horse to the King of Egypt, who leads it off the stage and returns at once. St. George plants one foot on the Dragon's body (perhaps it wriggles a little !) and strikes an heroic attitude.*]

St. George. Here I am, St. George, that worthy champion bold,

And with my sword and spear I've won three crowns of gold :

I've found the fiery Dragon, and brought him to the slaughter ;

By that I've won fair Sabra, the King of Egypt's daughter.

[*The Turkish Knight advances.*]

Turkish Knight. Here come I, the Turkish Knight,

Come from the Turkish land to fight.

I'll fight St. George, who is my foe,

I'll make him yield before I go :

He brags to such a high degree,

He thinks there's none can do the like of he.

    St. George. Where is the Turk that will before me stand ?

I'll cut him down with my courageous hand.

    [*They fight. The Dragon crawls apprehensively out of their way. The Turkish Knight is overcome, and falls on one knee.*]

    Turkish Knight. Oh ! pardon me, St. George, pardon of thee I crave.

Oh ! pardon me this night, and I will be thy slave.

    St. George. I'll never pardon a Turkish Knight ;

So rise thee up again, and try thy might.

    [*They fight again, and the Knight is killed. Father Christmas comes forward again and looks at the body.*]

    Father Christmas. Is there a doctor to be found

All ready, near at hand,

To cure a deep and deadly wound

And make the champion stand ?

    [*Re-enter the Doctor with his physic.*]

    Doctor. Ah ! yes, there is a doctor to be found,

All ready, near at hand,

To cure a deep and deadly wound

And make the champion stand.

    Father Christmas. What can you cure ?

    Doctor. All sorts of diseases,

Whatever you pleases,

The phthisic, the palsy, and the gout ;

Whatever disorder, I'll soon pull him out.

    Father Christmas. What is your fee ?

    Doctor. Fifteen pounds, it is my fee,

The money to lay down ;

But as 'tis such a rogue as he,

I'll cure him for ten pound.

I have a little bottle of Elicumpane,
Here, Jack, take a little of my flip-flop,

> [*He opens the Turkish Knight's jaws and pours in some of his medicine.*]

Pour it down thy tip-top,
Rise up and fight again.

> [*The Turkish Knight chokes and sneezes violently and rises to his feet. St. George advances on him, and he hurriedly takes refuge behind Father Christmas. The Doctor holds out his hand to Father Christmas for his fee, and receives a push that sends him staggering back. The Fool dances in carrying a large basin labelled " Girdy Grout " and thrusts it into the Doctor's hands. Father Christmas kicks him hard, and he runs out, the Fool following and belabouring him. Father Christmas addresses the audience.*]

Father Christmas. Now, ladies and gentlemen,
Your sport is just ended,
So prepare for the pan which is highly commended.

> [*Enter the Fool, as Beelzebub, wearing a mask, and carrying a heavy club and a frying-pan.*]

Fool. In comes I, old Beelzebub ;
Over my shoulder I carry my club,
And in my hand a frying-pan,
Pleased to get all the money I can.

> [*He goes down into the audience and takes a collection in the frying-pan, while the other characters group themselves about Father Christmas, the Dragon having come to life again and the Doctor sneaked in apprehensively. They sing in chorus.*]

Girdy Grout, Coarse gruel. It is a traditional part of the play that the Doctor should be given this, kicked, and driven out.

CHORUS.

Hold, men, hold !
We are very cold,
Inside and outside,
We are very cold.
If you don't give us silver,
Then give us gold
From the money in your pockets—
Hold, men, hold !

[*St. George and the Dragon were on the point of
coming to blows again, but at the last line,
which was sung very vigorously and pointedly,
they were separated, with many threatening
gestures.*]

Hold, men, hold !
Put up your sticks,
End all your tricks ;
Hold, men, hold !
Hold, men, hold !

[*If the collection is being taken really, not in
pretence, the Chorus should be repeated to give
the Fool time to go round, or a folk-song and
dance introduced. Then all the characters,
led by Father Christmas, file out through the
audience, singing as they go.*]

CHORUS.

Merry, merry Christmas !—Hold, men, hold !—
Be there loaf in your locker and sheep in your
    fold,

A fire on your hearth and a pudding in your pot,
Money in your pocket and good luck for your lot !
Money in your pocket, silver and gold,
And a merry, merry Christmas !—Hold, men,
    hold !
    [*Their voices die away in the distance.*]

CURTAIN

COMMENTARY

NAOMI MITCHISON : ELFEN HILL

When you have read this play you may feel that the author has been to Elfland herself, and writes only of what she has seen and heard, and when you have read her novels and tales, one day, you may wonder still more whether she has lived in ancient Greece and Rome and the England that the Romans knew ; for Mrs. Mitchison " walks at ease through the centuries," and seems to know countries far away in time and place as you know your own home and school. This is a great and rare gift of hers. It has enabled her to give us here something of the true magic and poetry of the Elfen Kingdom, with a touch of sadness and a touch of humour too. You should certainly read some of her other plays and stories.

ON TALKING IT OVER

1. Do you think that Prince Garamond ever wished himself back in Elfen Hill ? Do you think he ever tried to go back ?

2. How was it that the Queen was able to enter Elfen Hill and return in safety with Garamond ?

3. Do you know any other story in which a prisoner escapes from fairyland, or a mortal has to guess fairy riddles ? If so, tell it to the class.

4. In her Foreword to *Nix-Nought-Nothing* Mrs.

Mitchison writes, " The stories of the plays are all more or less traditional, and based on Joseph Jacobs' books of Fairy Tales, which I had read to me twenty years ago, have been reading aloud for the last five, and which I used to read to myself in the interval." What does this tell you about her ?

5. Can you tell from the verse of this play what poems the author has been reading ? This is not an easy question, but if you have read any of the poems yourself you may be able to guess.

FOR PEN AND PENCIL

6. Write the scene, described by the Nurse, in which the Elfen King carries off Garamond. It should be partly or entirely in verse, and you may introduce one or more characters besides the three already named. It might be a good plan to talk this over in class before you begin.

7. Write a letter from the Chamberlain to the Old King whom he wanted the Queen to marry, telling him that Garamond had returned and forbidden the marriage. If you read the Chamberlain's speeches again carefully you will be able to imagine how he would write. Use as many long words as you can, looking them up in the dictionary if you are not sure of them. It will be fun inventing long-winded beginnings and endings to the letter, not " Dear King," of course, or " Yours Affectionately," but something in this style : " To His Most Serene, Illustrious, and Magnipotent Majesty, King Puffalot. . . ."

8. Draw and paint Rushy Brook or Elfen Hill as they are described in the play ; or, better still, make model stage-settings for them. You will find a note about model theatres in Section 79.

BOOKS TO READ

9. *Nix-Nought-Nothing*, by Naomi Mitchison. (Jonathan Cape.) *Elfen Hill* is one of the four plays in this volume.

The Hostages, by Naomi Mitchison. (Jonathan Cape.) Stories for boys and girls.

Tam Lin, a play in *Ballads and Ballad-Plays*, Teaching of English Series. (Uniform with this volume.)

Tales from Andersen and Grimm, Tales from the Arabian Nights. Two more volumes in this series, with many pictures.

KITTY BARNE : PETER AND THE CLOCK

Miss Kitty Barne, who is Mrs. Eric Streatfeild, has written a number of good plays for young players, several of them musical plays. She likes writing about the past, and into this little comedy she has packed a surprising number of references to Victorian ideas which now seem quaint to us—just as many of our ideas and doings will seem funny or absurd to the people of the twenty-first century. So the play is not only amusing, it gives us an interesting glimpse of the life of boys and girls a hundred years ago.

ON TALKING IT OVER

10. Guess the meaning of negus, Gregory, a Tiger and a Cornet, after looking carefully at the speeches in which they are used. Then look them up in an encyclopædia or dictionary.

11. What is " righteous indignation " ?

12. Say what you think of Fanny and Peter.

13. Whom was Victoria named after?

14. What differences between 1840 and the present time have you discovered from the play? Do you wish that you had lived then? Is there any past age in which you would have rather lived than the present?

15. Do you think that Peter would have behaved in real life as he does in the play?

FOR PEN AND PENCIL

16. Write about the differences mentioned in Section 14.

17. Write a little scene in which mamma discovers the murder and the three children are called in.

18. Draw the grandfather clock.

BOOKS TO READ

19. *Philemon and Baucis*, by Kitty Barne. (Gowans and Gray.) A one-act play based on the Greek legend. *Susie pays a Visit*, a fairy comedy in one act. *The Amber Gate*, a pageant play of boys and girls from David to Jack Cornwell, in 22 episodes. By Kitty Barne. (Curwen.)

Daisy's Ball and *Mr. Poulter's Sword*, in *Plays from Literature*, Junior Book, by Evelyn Smith. *Boys and Girls of Fiction* (First and Second Series). All three volumes uniform with this.

JOHN DRINKWATER: ROBIN HOOD AND THE PEDLAR

Once upon a time Mr. Drinkwater was one of a small company of amateur actors in Birmingham, who called themselves the Pilgrim Players and visited many towns and villages to perform their plays. Now they have grown and changed into a well-known professional company, the Birmingham Repertory Theatre, and Mr. Drinkwater has become a famous dramatist and poet, author of *Abraham Lincoln, Oliver Cromwell, Bird in Hand*, and other plays which have been performed all over the world.

Robin Hood and the Pedlar was written in 1914 for performance in the open air, and it is one of the few good plays of the kind. Mr. Drinkwater found a hero after his own heart in Robin Hood, who has been growing more and more popular since people first began to write songs and ballads about him more than five hundred years ago.* Some historians say that he lived in the twelfth century, others maintain that he never existed, but we may cheerfully leave it to them to discuss the matter, because we know that nowadays at least he is very much alive, in the immortal company of Robinson Crusoe, the Pied Piper, King Arthur, Peter Pan, and Sherlock Holmes, and all our other heroes of story and legend.

ON TALKING IT OVER

20. Why does Little John call the magpies " lying little chickens " ?

21. What do you think of the Sheriff ? Is he altogether a coward ?

22. Is this a play of real life, like *Peter and the Clock*, or a fairy-tale play, like *Elfen Hill* ?

23. Choose two speakers from the class to represent the prison porter and the " sour fellow on guard," and let them argue as to which is to blame for letting the ballad-singer escape.

* "I know rhymes of Robin Hood," says one of the characters in "Piers the Plowman," a long poem written by William Langland about 1377.

24. Choose three speakers to represent Robin Hood, the Sheriff, and the King, and let them have a three-cornered talk, the Sheriff accusing Robin Hood and defending himself, and so on. Not more than one may speak at once!

25. " A man who hates a good song is no fit man to hold a King's power," says the ballad-singer.

Shakespeare puts it even more strongly in *The Merchant of Venice* :

> " The man that hath no music in himself,
>   Nor is not moved with concord of sweet sounds,
> Is fit for treasons, stratagems, and spoils ;
> The motions of his spirit are dull as night
> And his affections dark as Erebus.*
> Let no such man be trusted."

What do you think of this ? What happens to people who dislike beautiful things or never notice them ? What happens to people who are always compelled to live in ugly, noisy places ? Have you noticed any places growing uglier and noisier in the past year or two ? Have you heard people saying that England is getting uglier ? Does it matter very much ? Now perhaps you want to ask your teacher questions!

26. Would you like the play better if there were no fairies in it ? Would it be easy to leave them out in a performance ?

27. What difference would it make to the play if it were all in prose ?

FOR PEN AND PENCIL

28. Draw or describe the dress worn by the outlaws.

29. Find in a history or encyclopædia a picture of a bow and arrow, copy the picture, and write a short

---

* Erebus is part of the dark underworld of the dead in the ancient Greek stories.

account of them, saying what they were made of, and so on. There are a good many people in England nowadays named Fletcher and Archer. Why?

30. Find out all you can about the King: when he lived, why he was called Lionheart, why he went abroad, who ruled England while he was away, etc. Then write what you have learned, under the title, " Richard Cœur-de-Lion."

31. Write the story of any other adventure which befell the King or Robin Hood.

32. After class discussion, write a short play about Robin Hood. You might very well use the story of one of the Robin Hood ballads in *Ballads and Ballad-Plays*, or a story from *Told in Sherwood*.

BOOKS TO READ

33. *Robin Hood and the Potter* and the ballads of Robin Hood in *Ballads and Ballad-Plays* (T.E.S.). Uniform with this volume.

Robin Hood, by Alfred Noyes, in *Eight Modern Plays* (T.E.S.).

Robin Hood, by J. C. Squire. (Heinemann.) A five-act play written for open-air performance.

The Greenwood, edited by Sir Henry Newbolt (T.E.S.), Tales of Robin Hood from Scott's *Ivanhoe*, " A Lyttell Geste of Robin Hood," etc.

Told in Sherwood, by Hugh Chesterman. The story of the outlaw's whole career, told in simple modern English, with twelve illustrations by Mrs. Frank Rogers (T.E.S.). Uniform with this volume.

W. GRAHAM ROBERTSON : ARCHIBALD

As in *Eight Modern Plays*, we cannot do better than allow the author to explain, in his own inimitable way,

how he came to write *Archibald* and the other two
plays which make up the volume entitled *The Slippers
of Cinderella*.

" I have often been told," he writes, " that to find
suitable plays for children is a difficult task, but such
has not been my experience. While trying to meet
the demands of a company of infant actors, ranging
from six to thirteen, I came across suitable plays by
the score ; plays good and bad, comic and tragic, but
all of a uniform and depressing suitability.

" The suitable plays were charming, they were
childlike, there was nothing in them to which any
one could object, but—I regarded the members of
my troupe dispassionately. They were charming certainly, but there was plenty to object to in all of them,
and were they childlike ?

" Of what interest to my volcanic leading lady, a
strong, emotional actress rising ten and already with
an eye on Lady Macbeth, were the pastoral but puny
woes of Little Bo-Peep ? What in common had my
elegantly fastidious Jeune Premier of eight with
Tommy Tucker or Little Jack Horner, whose table
manners had long since caused him to drop their
acquaintance ? All had left the nursery far, far
behind, from the youngest extra lady to the veteran
tottering soberly into her teens, and their point of view
seemed identical with that of the adult Thespian.

" What they wanted was an unsuitable play, and
they looked to me to provide one ; a play that should
be neither idyllic, infantine, nor improving. Hang it
all—as the troupe very naturally felt—why improve-
ment ?

" Hence, therefore, the Theatre of the Children's
Troupe, of which the three following plays are speci-
mens. Their general tone is low, their language
unrefined, they contain no elements of poetry or
morality, they could not by any possibility improve
anybody ; in a word, they can be confidently recom-

mended to juvenile actors as entirely and absolutely unsuitable."

ON TALKING IT OVER

34. Which part would you like to take, and why ?

35. Do you think the author wants us to believe that all this really happened, or could happen ; or does he simply want to amuse us ? When you have given your answer, can you give your reasons ?

36. Early in the play Jack says, " I've got some boys' clothes here that my cousin lent me to take home for theatricals—I wish I might wear 'em." Why did the author put this in ? Why did he put it in here and not later ? Can you find any other speeches which were written for a similar reason ?

37. The author of a play is called a *playwright* not a play-writer. What is the difference ? Has this question any connection with Section 36 ?

38. Are there any speeches in the play which show it was written a few years ago ? If so, how would you alter them to bring them up to date ?

39. Are you sorry for Midge ?

FOR PEN AND PENCIL

40. Write what you think of Midge, Jack, Julia, and Archibald.

41. Write what Midge and Archibald said to each other in the cab on the way to the station, arranging the speeches as in a play, with the speaker's name at the beginning of each. And if you think that it ended with a tussle on the floor of the cab, or something of the kind, then put that in as a stage-direction !

BOOKS TO READ

42. *The Slippers of Cinderella*, by W. Graham Robertson, in *Eight Modern Plays* (T.E.S.).
Four Plays for Children, by Beatrice Mayor. (Blackwell.)

A. P. HERBERT : FAT KING MELON

It is not Mr. Herbert's only claim to distinction that he is (or was) the best-dressed man in Hammersmith. Not long ago he made the even more interesting claim that he was (or is) the most industrious man in London. He writes novels and plays and verses, he contributes regularly to *Punch* and other periodicals, and all that he does is good, for besides being one of the most industrious he is one of the cleverest and most amusing writers of the day. So we may be grateful that he has not been *too* industrious to find time for this witty little comedy, which is even better when it is acted than when it is read—and that is one of the true tests of a play, is it not ?

ON TALKING IT OVER

43. What have you learned about the play from the Prologue and the notice of the first performance ?

44. Do you know where Mr. Herbert found the last line of Fairy Mumbo's opening song ?

45. What kind of play is this ? Have you seen or read any other which stops at intervals while the characters sing about themselves ?

46. Imagine that you are King Melon or Princess

Caraway, and tell the class the story of your adventures. (Don't be *too* solemn about it.)

FOR PEN AND PENCIL

47. Draw or describe the ship in Scene iv., and explain how you would make it.
48. Write a short scene in which Fairy Mumbo sees another patient.
49. Write another Prologue for a performance of this play by your own class or dramatic society, or another song for any of the characters to sing.
50. Draw and paint a picture of any scene in the play.

BOOKS TO READ

51. *The Princess and the Woodcutter*, by A. A. Milne, in *Eight Modern Plays*.
The Dyspeptic Ogre, by Percival Wilde.
Susie pays a Visit, by Kitty Barne.

ELIZABETH McFADDEN: WHY THE CHIMES RANG

When English drama first began, about a thousand years ago, it was with simple little religious plays that were acted in church at Easter and Christmas as part of the service, and represented the birth and death and resurrection of our Lord. The priests thought that this was a good way of teaching these stories to their people, most of whom could neither read nor write.

These plays became so popular that they had to be given in the churchyards, to make room for the crowds who flocked to see them. Then they moved on to the market squares, with craftsmen and tradesmen as players instead of the monks and priests, and as more and more plays were written they became longer, less religious, and more humorous, until the first English theatres were built in the reign of Elizabeth, Shakespeare and others wrote great comedies and tragedies, and religious plays became rare.

Nowadays, however, they have become popular again, chiefly because there has been a great revival of amateur acting, and they are being performed in church halls and churches and even in Canterbury Cathedral. Some are the beautiful old plays written in the Middle Ages. Others are by modern dramatists and include many Christmas plays, such as this which Miss McFadden has made from a short story by Professor Alden. It has been performed hundreds of times in the United States (both authors are Americans), in Canada, Hawaii, and Japan, and is now becoming popular in England too, for it has caught much of the spirit of Christmas.

ON TALKING IT OVER

52. Why was Holger's gift accepted? Why were the others rejected?

53. We are not told who the Woman was. Can you make any suggestions?

54. What do you like best in the play?

FOR PEN AND PENCIL

55. Write any Christmas story, or describe any cathedral or church that you know, or copy and paint the pictures on pages 206 and 208.

BOOKS TO READ

56. *The Travelling Man*, a Christmas mystery play by Lady Gregory. (Putnam's.)

The Three Kings, a little nativity play in *Ballads and Ballad-Plays* (T.E.S.).

Their Angels, a modern nativity play by V. A. Pearn. (Samuel French.)

Michael, by Miles Malleson. In *Eight Modern Plays* (T.E.S.).

ROBIN HOOD AND FRIAR TUCK

This rough-and-tumble old play, which was first printed (so far as we know) about 1550, makes a striking contrast with the modern plays and will remind you of the Robin Hood ballads.

Besides putting in all the stage directions, the editor has changed the old spelling and punctuation and altered several lines so that the play may be easier to act and read. Perhaps you will make further alterations and additions of your own, as suggested below.

ON TALKING IT OVER

57. Would you know that this is an old play if you had not been told. If so, how?

58. What is a folk-play?

59. Is this play very different from *Robin Hood and the Pedlar*? Does this Robin Hood seem to you to be a different kind of man from Mr. Drinkwater's hero?

60. What do you like about the play ? What are its weak points ? Are there any improvements or additions which you wish to make ? For example, it is a pity, don't you think, that, except for Little John's short speech, all the talking is done by Robin Hood and Friar Tuck. Speeches for other characters might be written, and the plot made more interesting.

61. Is it a good thing for a character to introduce himself to the audience, as Friar Tuck does ?

FOR PEN AND PENCIL

62. After talking over the points suggested in Section 60, rewrite the play, or parts of it, to make your own acting version.

63. Write a short speech in verse for Robin Hood so that he can introduce himself to the audience, as Friar Tuck does, when he first appears.

BOOKS TO READ

64. *Robin Hood and the Potter*, a ballad-play in *Ballads and Ballad-Plays*.

Robin Hood and the Potter, an old folk-play, with a chapter about Robin Hood plays, in *Earlier English Drama*, edited by F. J. Tickner (T.E.S.).

ST. GEORGE AND THE DRAGON

This is by far the oldest and in many ways the most interesting play in this book, for it has come to us from the far distant past before the speech we know began to be spoken in this island, handed down by word of mouth, through generation after generation, and so changing steadily, as ballads and plays and stories always do when they depend upon people's memories. It is still acted in some parts of England ; while these words are being written, villagers in Sussex and the Cotswolds, at least, are rehearsing their own local versions for performance at Christmas, 1930. It was being acted in 1473, for one of the famous *Paston Letters*, written in that year, mentions a servant who was kept " to pleye Seynte Jorge and Robyn Hod and the Shryff off Nottyngham." And it is claimed that the Overton troupe of mummers in Hampshire has had a continuous existence of nearly eight hundred years. The play has been acted in many parts of England, Wales, Scotland, and Ireland in many different versions, several of which the editor has put together to make the play in this book, for though it seems not to have been written down until a hundred years ago, there are now twenty or thirty editions of the St. George play published.

If by magic we could travel back through the centuries, to follow the mummers stumping along to the squire's house or the baron's hall on Christmas Eve or 23rd April, we should find that the plot, the characters and the dialogue slowly changed, and that the further back we went in time the less the performance resembled the play we know. The Turkish Knight, for instance, must have appeared when English soldiers who had been fighting in the Crusades came home again full of strange tales. Perhaps the Fool and Beelzebub strayed in from other folk-plays. And if we went back far enough, still following the play, we should find that all the performances were in spring, not at Christmas, that all the characters had strange names, and that one of them was an old heathen god who had to be killed and brought to life again, as a magic way of making sure that spring would follow winter and the fields give good crops. Such dramas were once part of the religion of all the peoples around the Mediterranean Sea, and even to-day a play like our St. George play * is acted by Greek peasants in the vale of Tempe.

So you see that our Christmas mumming-play is not only a piece of good fun, it comes to us out of the distant past, bringing strange memories.

ON TALKING IT OVER

65. Can you tell from the play itself that it is old ?

66. Is the verse like that of the old ballads or like that of modern poems ?

67. Choose one of the characters and describe the dress which you would make for him.

68. Show the class how you would die if you were the Dragon.

FOR PEN AND PENCIL

69. In some versions the King of Egypt s daughter, the Princess Sabra, appears, and the King gives her hand to St. George when he has defeated the Dragon and the Turkish Knight. Write a very short scene about this, to be added to the play.

70. In the olden days Christmas used to be celebrated with much merriment and feasting, a great Yule log on the hearth, a boar's head on the table, and so on, and in the country visits from the mummers acting this old play were a regular part of the festivities.

Describe such a performance in the hall of the squire's house, with all his servants and half the village crowding in to watch and make remarks and applaud. You will have to imagine it all clearly before you can describe it.

* The legend of St. George and the Dragon probably grew out of the Greek myth of Perseus, an instance of how one story changes into another.

71. Write two or three verses of a song for the actors to sing while the Fool is going round with the frying-pan.

72. Draw and paint a real St. George and a fearsome Dragon (the picture on a pound note will help a little), paste them on cardboard or fretwood, and then cut them out and mount them so that they can fight properly. It is not much extra trouble to make them with movable heads and limbs.

BOOKS TO READ

73. *The Peace Egg.* A Yorkshire St. George Play. (Oxford Press.)

The chapters on Christmastide Plays and Mummers and Gleemen in *Earlier English Drama* (T.E.S.).

A Christmas Epilogue, in *Eight Modern Plays* (T.E.S.).

The Reluctant Dragon, in *Dream Days*, by Kenneth Grahame (T.E.S.).

The description of the Mumming Play in *The Return of the Native*, by Thomas Hardy, Book II., Chapters IV. and V. This might be read to the class, with some abridgment.

Christmas at Dingley Dell, in Chapter XXVIII. of *The Pickwick Papers*, by Charles Dickens.

GENERAL

74. Describe an amusing incident, or an exciting incident, in any one of the plays.

75. Draw, paint, and cut out scenery for one of the plays, and set it up as it would be on the stage. If you can make the characters as well, so much the better.

76. Which character in the book are you most interested in, and why?

77. Draw up a programme of two, three, or four of the plays, according to the number of actors available, for performance by your own form or society. Choose and arrange the plays carefully to make a good and varied programme. Then cast the plays (that is, choose the actors), giving every person available the part for which he or she is best suited, omitting no one, and giving two parts to one player only if it is unavoidable. A play which cannot be cast fairly well should not be put in the programme.

78. Which plays in this book would you choose for performance (a) in the open air, (b) in church, (c) at school speech-day, (d) at Christmas, (e) at a family party held in a small room.

79. Make a model theatre, with help from some one older if you need it. Full instructions are given in *Everybody's Theatre*, written and illustrated by H. W. Whanslaw (Wells Gardner, Darton). With some one helping you to manage the characters and read the parts behind the scenes, you can perform several of the plays in this book on your model stage.

ACTING NOTES

DETAILED notes on production, acting and stage-management are given in other volumes in this series, especially *Eight Modern Plays* and *Nine Modern Plays*, and some principles of dramatic work with children are formulated in *Ballads and Ballad-Plays*, which is uniform with this volume. Miss McFadden's acting appendix to *Why the Chimes Rang*, which is reprinted in full on pages 192–210, contains much admirable advice on how to approach problems of production and staging. Space permits only brief notes on the other plays.

ELFEN HILL

No performance of this play may be given unless permission has been obtained in advance from Messrs. Jonathan Cape, Ltd., 30 Bedford Square, London, W.C.I. The usual fee for amateurs is one and a half guineas.

The play takes about forty minutes.

The author's stage-directions are so complete and admirable that they leave hardly anything to be said. Part of her Foreword may be quoted : " All the indoor plays should be as simple as possible ; in each of them only one plain-coloured curtain or hanging at the back is needed, with the least possible indication of change of scene. I have given some idea of how this may be done, also of dresses and properties, but obviously most can be left to the individual producer or nursery. In *Hobyah! Hobyah!* and *Elfen Hill* it is fairly clear that, in several places, the actors can say what they please, keeping the plays up to date according to their own ideas."

For general advice on dresses for this and the other costume plays, see page 204.

It is of great importance that the intervals between the scenes should be very short, and to secure this the scene-changing must be planned and *rehearsed* in detail, each scene-shifter having specific duties assigned to him.

However elementary the lighting installation may be, an effort should be made to provide green light for the last scene—from a few bulbs dipped in lacquer or from one or two flood-lights (made from biscuit tins) with green gelatine slides. Good lighting is of the greatest artistic value.

There is no other play in this book, with the doubtful exception of *St. George and the Dragon*, in which it is so important that the young players should be given every possible freedom in interpretation ; they know more of elfland than any adult producer can remember.

PETER AND THE CLOCK

This play is fully protected by copyright, and no performance may be given unless permission has first been obtained from Miss Kitty Barne, c/o Messrs. J. Curwen and Sons, Ltd., 24 Berners Street, London, W.1.

No fee is usually charged except for performances in theatres or public halls.

The play takes about twenty-five minutes.

The author has visualized her setting and characters in considerable detail, which the producer will do well to follow. She has added a helpful note on the dresses :

"*Fanny.*—An elaborate ball-dress, very full skirt looped up with rosebuds ; white muslin trousers tied at the ankle ; very short puff sleeves and low neck ; white stockings and black slippers. Either one-button kid gloves or mittens. Her hair parted in the middle and curled in ringlets on either side of her face.

"*Peter.*—Short jacket of dark blue cloth ; white collar and big tie. Trousers tight round the leg and stopping six inches short of the ankle ; white socks ; black slippers.

"*Victoria.*—Full, rather long skirt ; rather tight bodice with short sleeves and low neck ; black alpaca apron ; white stockings and black slippers. Her hair is parted in the middle and worn in a chenille net at the back."

For further help with the dresses, the producer cannot do better than consult *English Children's Costume since 1775*, by Iris Brooke (Black), which is delightfully illustrated in colour by the author.

As it is extremely important that the interval between the two scenes should be as short as possible, dresses for the players to change into must be ready in the wings. Peter and Victoria can wear their loose nightdresses over their other clothes, unless it is found advisable for Peter to remove his jacket. Fanny has longer to change, and should have no difficulty with clothes, but it is not likely that there will be time to put her hair into curl papers. She should have two wigs, or have her hair in curl papers from the first, but completely covered by her skirt.

If the play is acted in a curtain set, as it may well be, the "ginger-coloured curtains" hung over the others will be sufficient indication of the window. They will be drawn over the imaginary window, and Peter will merely peep through them.

There should be no difficulty in borrowing Victorian

or Victorian-looking furniture from an antique dealer. Owing to the importance of the clock it should be a genuine antique. The whirr, from a small revolving rattle, and the striking, from a deep-noted gong, must be done behind the stage, but for the first scene the clock may be set going, with its striking apparatus out of action and the metronome synchronized with its ticking, provided that the scene has been carefully timed so that the clock points approximately to six when the fly arrives. In a large hall, where the hands cannot be clearly seen, this will be unnecessary. The glass over the clock face might be slightly blurred with vaseline.

The play should be produced as realistically as possible, in the spirit of intent seriousness that is natural to children. A discrepancy of several years between the ages of the players and the ages of the characters will be covered by the dresses and the differences in nursery régime.

ROBIN HOOD AND THE PEDLAR

No performance of this play may be given unless permission has been obtained in advance from the author's agents, Messrs. Samuel French, 26 Southampton Street, Strand, London, W.C.2. The fee is one guinea for each amateur performance.

The play takes about forty-five minutes.

Mr. Drinkwater says of this and his other "Masques" that they " were written expressly for performance by a large number—between two and three hundred—of Messrs. Cadbury's work-people at Bourneville. The greatest simplicity of mass effect in the open air was aimed at, and a technique that would be within the acting resources of a large and enthusiastic but unskilled company of amateurs." The concluding phrase describes any class of boys and girls, whose love of acting and movement and adventure, with their instinctive sense of poetry, will do much to compensate for their lack of skill.

The keynote of the play is romantic poetry, not realism, but it must be produced with gusto as well as imagination. The ideal setting is the edge of a wood or a shrubbery, where real trees and bushes provide the players with " wings " and a background. The absence of a front curtain presents no difficulty at all. Robin Hood comes on alone at the beginning, and all troop off at the end. For indoor performances a stage hung with green curtains will serve, preferably with shrubs and greenery, and the forest may be suggested by narrow strips of a brown and green material, such as casement cloth, hung at intervals towards the back of the stage so that the players may pass among them.

The outlaws' dress is simple and graceful : tunics, shorts, and stockings of green—the stockings being cheap white ones, home dyed ; socks with their tops rolled down almost to the ankles for boots ; felt hats cut down, or close-fitting caps, decked with feathers. Belts, pouches, daggers, etc., can be of bright contrasting colours. All these may well be made at home, with little trouble, and so may bows and arrows; boys enjoy making them, and should be encouraged to search all available books for information. Instructions for making all the dresses will be found in *The Bankside Costume Book.*

There are coloured pictures by Walter Crane in *Robin Hood and his Merry Men* (Nelson), and outline drawings in *Told in Sherwood* (Nelson).

The fire may be imaginary, though it requires only a little ingenuity and care for one of the players to bring on a great armful of sticks concealing a red electric light bulb or two with trailing wires, from which he can build a fire. The wire must be carefully disposed so that there is the minimum of danger of it tripping any one in the latter part of the play. If one of the sleeping outlaws lies so as to mask the fire, he can disconnect the wire so that it can be drawn into the wings. The arrow, which " quivers in the ground," may be thrown by hand from the wings to fall near the Sheriff; if it is sharp enough to quiver in the floor of the stage it will be dangerous. The quarter-staff combats, carefully rehearsed, should not be dangerous, especially if hand-guards of wire, leather, or plain linoleum can be made, or gloves worn. The combats, songs, and dances must be carefully rehearsed with the remainder of the action. If necessary, however, it is easy to omit the dances and the fairies, and the Pedlar might crown himself in the darkness.

A pastoral performance should be rehearsed in the open air as far as possible, because it is most important to make sure that the players' voices carry and because the dramatic values involved are so different.

The music specially written for this play by James Brier is no longer available, having been destroyed by fire while still in MS., so the producer will have to find his own settings for the songs, unless he omits them— which would be a pity.

ARCHIBALD

For the condition on which amateur performances of this play may be given see the note on page 67. There is no acting fee.

The play takes about forty-five minutes.

This is an excellent farce for girls, and could not be easier to stage. Even the fire is out! A "curtain set" will serve admirably if there is no realistic box-set available, and the door need be no more than an opening in the curtains. If the dancing is " cut," which would be a pity, even the piano can be dispensed with and the furniture reduced to a few chairs and a table covered with a cloth. A fireplace is very desirable, however. It is easy to construct, and should be made to stand by itself, so that—with slight disguises—it can be used repeatedly in various settings. Grey and black paper screwed into balls will make the dead embers of the fire.

No doubt the author will forgive the producer who brings the dialogue up to date at a few points, and the players will probably be ready to suggest topical allusions—which may have to be censored by authority!

The play is as frankly farcical and theatrical as it is amusing, and should be produced for effect, not for realism, though over-acting must be controlled by discretion. Farce is always difficult for amateurs of any age, more difficult than any other dramatic form except perhaps poetic tragedy, because it depends so much upon skill in acting, sureness of touch, and smoothness of performance. This farce, however, was written by an able playwright for a company of girls, and any such company may attempt it with confidence if they rehearse the play thoroughly. Smooth running without gap or delay must be secured, and while speech, movement, and characterization must not be neglected, it is all important to see that cues are taken instantly (so difficult to maintain) and entrances and exits exactly timed. This is, among other things, excellent training in teamwork. If what is learned in rehearsal is not to be lost in performance, it is important that from the first the stage should be marked out (if it cannot be set) in the dimensions of the setting, with the furniture correctly placed.

When the actresses are word-perfect, and the play is nicely timed and in good mechanical " going order," producer and cast may confidently settle down to develop all those finer points of delivery and movement which bring the whole thing to life. They will then appreciate the skill with which the play has been written, and the wit of the dialogue.

FAT KING MELON

No performance of this play may be given unless permission has been obtained in advance from the Oxford University Press, Oxford.

The play takes about forty minutes.

The producer who wishes to do full justice to this drama of *Fat King Melon and Princess Caraway* cannot do better than begin by attending one or more, preferably more, of Sir Nigel Playfair's delectable productions at the Lyric Theatre, Hammersmith. Mr. Herbert has had his share in a number of them, and this play is in the Lyric tradition, the tradition of *The Beggar's Opera, Riverside Nights, When Crumbles Played, The Critic,* and *Tantivy Towers,* which are among the best entertainments that London has seen since the war.

But the producer who has had no opportunity of studying Sir Nigel Playfair's methods need not hesitate to attempt *Fat King Melon*, provided that he approaches it in the right spirit. It should be treated as a great " lark " which has to be acted seriously in order to get all the possible fun out of it, yet with a seriousness, never dull or plodding, that is light of touch because of its undercurrent of enjoyment and humour. Most children whose spontaneity is not chilled by repression will find the right note instinctively, because they will be playing at kings and princesses and highwaymen, rather than playing them, and however intent and serious they may be, their own enjoyment of it all will be plain to themselves and to the audience. With the right note found, and careful rehearsal, the play is bound to be a success because of its wit and skill.

Staging may be as simple or as elaborate as desired. Simple settings will help to avoid long intervals, which should certainly be avoided in so short a play, and curtains will provide a sufficient background, with a little ingenuity. If the back curtain is in sections, part of it can be drawn aside for Scene i. to reveal the doorway (with strong wooden uprights) through which King Melon squeezes ; another section reveals the Great Gate of Scene ii., with a small portable flight of steps in front and a little platform behind, if desired, so that the Queen can make an imposing entrance ; plain curtain provides the background for Scenes iii. and v. ; and for the ship of Scene iv. the platform and steps could be used again, with cardboard bulwarks. A much more desirable ship, however, could be made with little trouble from a small wooden platform strong enough to bear the crew and the Princess, with sides of gaily painted cardboard or three-ply wood and a mast strong enough to carry a preposterous sail and a real pulley to which the Blue Peter can be hoisted. The anchor can be hauled on to the deck from the side of the stage. The gangway may consist of a stool, to be taken in when the Princess has gone aboard. If the ship is mounted on wheels the " rough sailors " can " go below " at the end of the scene, more or less masked by the ship's sides, and push it across the stage, to the great joy of every one concerned. Where conditions are favourable the discussion, designing, and making of this ship, perhaps with some help in the woodwork from senior school carpenters, can be a useful and enjoyable piece of handwork. (Would the ship have a figure-head, a picture on the sail, and so on ?)

Bright colours are needed for the play, especially if the background is to consist of the same curtain throughout, and the dresses should be in the gayest fairy-tale fashion, home-made from cheap materials and copied from fairy-tale pictures, such as Heath Robinson's illustrations to Hans Andersen.

WHY THE CHIMES RANG

Why the Chimes Rang was written for adult performance, and is the most difficult play in the book for little players—but not too difficult. It is perhaps unnecessary to add that boys and girls of eleven or so should not be drilled into realistic portrayals of an old woman, a middle-aged man, etc., even if this were practicable, but left as free as possible to give their own conception of these characters. Simplicity and sincerity are absolutely essential. Any affectation or " showing off " to the audience, unpleasant as they are in any play, would be disastrous and disgusting in this.

The author's detailed notes are given below:

The following suggestions for a simplified staging of *Why the Chimes Rang* are offered, not to college dramatic societies or other expert amateurs, but to the many young people in the secondary schools, Sunday schools, and country districts, who would enjoy staging short plays if it could be done without elaborate scenery or lighting equipment and without previous experience in stage management.

Simplicity aided by imagination goes far upon the stage, and it should always be remembered that the real aim is the creation of a given emotion in the minds of the audience rather than the creation of a given thing upon the stage. If a circle of gilt paper on the head of a fine-looking lad can create a vivid impression of kingly dignity, all the crown jewels of Europe cannot better the paper for stage purposes.

In producing a play, it should first be carefully read to see what main impression is to be conveyed, and what chief elements are to be emphasized to make up this impression. The details can then be worked out in harmony with the more important factors.

In *Why the Chimes Rang* religious exaltation is the mood to be created, and the divine beauty of charity is the main theme.

Three sharply contrasted effects are called for : the wood-cutter's hut, dark and humble ; and, set against this, the earthly splendour of the cathedral chancel, which in its turn is dimmed by the miraculous presence of the angel.

It is expected that this play will be adapted, by those giving it, to the form and degree of ritual desired. Censers and candles may be used or not, altar appointments and priestly vestments may be chosen to suit the taste of those concerned. Indeed, in all respects a play must be suited to the conditions under which it is presented and the audience before whom it is given ; and while the text may not be altered or added to, lines may be omitted if desired.

The information here given has been gathered from frequent working over of the material, but at best it can only help in a general way. Any one producing a play must work out his own problems in detail. One of the things that makes the staging of plays such fascinating work is the exercise it affords the imagination in overcoming obstacles.

SCENERY.—For the sake of facing the most difficult form of the problem of amateur staging, let us suppose that this play is to be given in a parlour or hall, without platform, without proscenium arch or curtains, with the walls, floor, and ceiling of such material and finish that no nails may be driven into them, and that the depth of the stage is only nine feet. It looks hopeless, but it can be done.

Under such conditions the only possible form of scenery is the screen. If the " scenery-man " is a bit of a carpenter, he can build the screens himself, making them as strong and as light as possible, with four leaves a few inches shorter than the height of the room in which they are to be used, and propor-

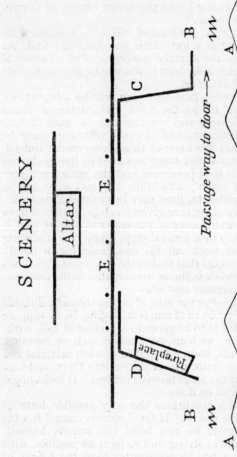

SCENERY

Altar

B

C

E

E

Passage way to door →

Front Line of Stage

D

Fireplace

B

A

Diagram showing the arrangement of screens for simplified staging of
Why the Chimes Rang.

tionately wide. The framework should be braced by
cross pieces in the middle of each leaf, and should
have stout leather handles nailed to them for con-
venience in lifting the screen. The right side should
be covered with canvas such as is used for scenery,
and the screens can then be easily repainted or re-
covered for later plays.

If it is not possible to have the screens made to
order, ordinary Japanese screens may be borrowed
or rented, and made to serve as front curtain and
framework for scenery.

Those indicated in the plan as A A and B B serve
as the front curtains, the centre sections (marked B B)
being drawn aside by persons stationed behind them
to show the interior of the hut when the play begins.
The four screens marked C D and E E form the walls
of the hut. In using screens it will be necessary to
do without the window and the actual door unless the
person in charge of the scenery is clever enough to
paint in a window on one panel of the screen and make
a door in another. If not, turn the end panel of the
screen marked C to run at right angles with the other
part, giving the impression of a passage with an ima-
gined door at the unseen end, and wherever in the
business of the parts the children are said to look
out of the window, let them instead look down this
passage, as though they were looking through the
open doorway.

On the right side of the room in the screen marked
D, a fireplace may be constructed by cutting away a
portion of the screen to suggest the line of the fireplace, putting behind this opening a box painted
black inside to represent the blackened chimney, and
finishing with a rough mantel stained brown to match
the wall tint. Of course, if the screens are borrowed
the fireplace will have to be dispensed with.

At the moment when the vision of the cathedral
is to appear, the screens marked E E are parted and

folded back, disclosing the chancel. Perhaps some church near by has stored in its basement an old stained-glass window, which may be borrowed and used as background for the church scene. Such a window was used in a performance of *Much Ado About Nothing* given some years ago at one of the Eastern colleges. It was dimly lit from behind by electric globes, and proved very successful in creating a churchly atmosphere. If this cannot be done, cover two of the tallest possible screens with any rich sombre-coloured drapery and stand them against the back wall. In the Los Angeles production the chancel was represented by a curtain of black velvet, flanked by two silver pillars, between them the altar. Black makes an exceedingly rich and effective foil for bright-coloured costumes. Whatever is used for backing in the chancel can be masked if unsatisfactory by Christmas greens, which should be arranged in long vertical lines that carry the eye up as high as possible and give a sense of dignity, or in the Gothic curves suggestive of church architecture.

[With care and patience an imitation stained-glass window can be made by sticking small pieces of coloured gelatine, paper, or silk upon a large panel of glass or celluloid, with black paper strips to represent the lead. The design of a real window can be copied. —EDITOR.]

Against this background, and in the centre of the space, place the altar. This can be made of a packing box painted gold or covered with suitable hangings. In one performance of this play a sectional bookcase which stood in the room was hung with purple cheese-cloth and served as an altar. Should the stage space be deep enough, broad steps before the shrine will give an added height to the priest and the angel.

If it is possible to have real scenery, the most illusive method of revealing and hiding the chancel is to have the back of the hut painted on a gauze drop, which is

backed by a black curtain.   [Photographs showing the
hut and the altar are given in the separate edition
of this play, which is published by Messrs. Samuel
French at 1s. 6d.—EDITOR.]   At the cue for showing
the chancel the lights in front of the gauze go out,
leaving the stage dark, then the black opaque curtain
is rolled up or drawn aside, and as the light is slowly
turned on the chancel the vision begins to take form
through the gauze, the latter becoming invisible and
transparent when there is no light in front of it.
The gauze prevents Holger from actually placing the
pennies in the priest's hand, but if the two approach
the gauze as though it were not there, and stretch
out their hands so that they seem to touch, the priest
being provided with additional pennies which he holds
up at the altar, no one in the audience would guess that
the coins had not been given him by the child.

Very few halls ostensibly built to house amateur
play-giving are adequate for the purpose.   Often the
stage is merely a shallow platform without curtains to
separate the actors from the audience, and the ceiling
and walls surrounding the stage are so finished that
the necessary screws for hanging curtains may not be
driven into them.   The amateur manager reaches the
depths of despair when he finds that even the floor of
the shallow platform offered him is of polished hard-
wood, and may not be marred by the screws of stage
braces.

Amateurs who have any voice in the preparation
of the stage being built for them should urge the
following specifications :

    1. The ceiling of the stage to be at least twice as
high as the proscenium arch.

    2. The depth of the stage to be at least fifteen feet,
deeper if the size of the place permits.

    3. The flooring, walls, and ceiling of the stage to be
of soft wood, into which nails and screws may be
driven ; or if the main construction is of brick, con-

crete, or metal, some inner wooden scaffolding or other overhead rigging capable of supporting scenery should be provided.

4. There should be some space on both sides of the stage for keeping scenery and properties to be used later in the play, and as a waiting-place for actors temporarily off the stage. The platform forming the stage proper should be continued over these wings so that actors leaving the scene may walk off on a level, and not seem to plunge cellarward in making their exits.

LIGHTING.—The important thing to be remembered about the lighting is the crescendo of light which occurs as the play runs its course. First the dim little hut so lit by the firelight, that the expressions on the faces of the actors can just be seen without straining the eyes of the audience. Then the rich but subdued lighting of the chancel, and finally the brilliant radiance shining on the angel.

Experiments with electricity should not be attempted by persons who do not understand its use, but if there is a competent electrician in the group putting on the play, use electric lighting by all means. No other form of light is so easily controlled or begins to give such effects for stage purposes.

The problems of theatre lighting differ with each set of conditions, and the best results can only be obtained by actual experiment with the means at hand. Do not feel that because you are an amateur, working with limited equipment, real beauty is beyond you. I have seen a stage picture approaching a Rembrandt in its charm of colouring and skilful use of shadows, created on a tiny stage with few appliances by an amateur who understood his lights.

If electricity is to be had, use three or four incandescent globes for the fire on the hearth, arranging logs of wood around them to simulate a fire. Additional lights as needed can be placed at the side off stage, or in the footlights; or, better, if the stage has a real proscenium these supplementary lights can be put in a " trough " that protects and intensifies them and hung overhead in the centre against the back of the proscenium arch.

As all these lights are to give a firelight effect, the incandescent globes should be dipped in a rich amber shade of colouring medium, which may be bought at any electrical supply house for about 5s. 6d. a pint. If gas or oil is used, a firelight effect can be obtained by slipping amber gelatine screens in front of the lamps. [Gelatines 22" × 17½" can be obtained for about 10d. each direct from makers of stage-lighting equipment, or through dealers.—EDITOR.]

If the fireplace cannot be made, then a charcoal brazier will serve as an excuse for light, and give a sense of warmth to the scene. The brazier can easily be made by any tinsmith from a piece of sheet iron supported on three legs, and there is an illustration of it in the right-hand corner of the scenery plate in Samuel French's edition of the play. An electric torch or even an ordinary lantern can be slipped inside the little stove to give out a faint glow. A piece of one of the amber screens put over the torch or lantern will warm the light, and the brazier can be placed anywhere in the hut.

The chancel may be lighted by a number of incandescent bulbs hidden at the sides of the scene, with the light so shielded that it shines on the altar and not into the hut. An especially effective place to put a strong light is inside the box representing the altar, with a hole cut in the top of the box so that the light shines up, giving a central radiance to the appointments of the altar and throwing into prominence the face and costume of each person who approaches it. If any of this light seems glaring it can be softened and diffused by masking it with amber or straw-coloured cheese-cloth.

Some form of searchlight is practically a necessity for producing the heavenly radiance that shines upon the angel. If procurable, a "baby spot-light" is the best appliance, but, lacking this, an automobile lamp and its battery can be used.

It is important that all light in the hut should go out when the vision of the chancel appears, so that the hut becomes merely an inner proscenium or dark frame around the rich picture of the altar. This, of course, does not mean that the lantern in the brazier need be extinguished, as the light given by that is negligible.

After the angel ceases speaking the tableau of the altar scene should be held as the music grows louder and louder through the final crescendo ; then, when the final note has been sung, blot out the stage by extinguishing all lights. Give a moment of darkness, during which the back wall of the hut is replaced, and the Old Woman slips out of the nearest opening in the scenery. Then turn on the front lights which illuminated the hut during the first part of the play.

MUSIC.—The three pieces of music required for this play are as follows :

The Sleep of the Child Jesus, part song for mixed voices by F. A. Gevaert.

Eightfold Alleluia composed for *Why the Chimes Rang*, by Percy Lee Atherton.

These two pieces come published together in a special edition for use with this play by the Boston Music Company. Price 15 cents per copy, post paid.

The bell movement (in five flats) (Postlude) by J. Guy Ropartz. Published by the Boston Music Company. Price 30 cents per copy, post paid.

For all the music, address the Boston Music Company, 116 Boylston Street, Boston, Mass. [Remittances should be sent by international money order ; or a dealer may be asked to obtain the music.—EDITOR.]

The pieces by Ropartz and Gevaert were chosen
for the Workshop production by Dr. A. T. Davison,
organist at Appleton Chapel, Harvard University,
and are admirably fitted to the play. Mr. Atherton's
Alleluia is also just what is needed, both in length
and in the triumphant crescendo which carries the
piece fittingly and dramatically to its close. It would
be difficult to replace this finale except by other
music written for the purpose.

The music is perhaps the most important single
element in the play. In the original version the
scene in the chancel was carried by dialogue, but
production showed the mistake. From the time that
the music begins, it, with the pantomimic action of
the actors, is all sufficient to interpret the mood and
meaning of the scene.

A small parlour organ is practically a necessity, and
can probably be procured for the cost of the cartage.

A choir of men's and women's voices is best for the
singing, but a good quartette will serve.

For the bells, the long tubular chimes which are
suspended by one end and struck with a wooden
hammer are the most satisfactory. If they seem too
metallic, try covering the head of the hammer with
folds of chamois skin. If such a set of chimes is not
to be had, a substitute can be found in the phonograph,
for which there are a number of chimes records. The
tune played on the phonograph must not be a modern
one ; Luther's hymn *Great God, what do I see and
hear?* (a Columbia record) is the best. The tune can
be disguised by lifting the needle occasionally and
setting it down gently on another part of the record.
As far as I know, no phonograph record presents
chimes pure and simple. It should be remembered,
however, that the phonograph record lacks the vitality
of tone and the note of jubilant triumph which a good
musician can bring from the bells themselves.

With the exception of the crescendo at the end

of the Alleluia, the music is kept soft and dreamy throughout. It is a temptation to try to achieve this effect by placing singers and organ back, off stage, so that the sound may come from a distance; but it has been found that the whole performance gains immeasurably if the organist is in front, where he can watch every movement of the actors and interpret them in his playing.

The music begins on Holger's speech, " Oh, thou art warm," and continues in one form or another throughout the play. The organist commences in the middle of the Ropartz *Sortie*, at the top of page 6, and continues this until the back of the hut is withdrawn, when he drifts into the accompaniment of the Gevaert song, and plays it through once without the voices. As Holger cries " Dame ! " and sinks back against the Woman's knee, this verse should end, and the voices of the choir take up the song with the organ.

From this point on every movement in the chancel is paced to the rhythm of the music. It has been found that a verse of the Gevaert song is just long enough to fit the following action.

A person in the procession enters the chancel, walks to the centre before the altar, kneels, and presents his gift to the priest. The priest accepts the gift, turns, goes up the steps to the altar, and raises the offering high above his head, holding it there a moment waiting for the chimes to ring, then brings his arms down, lays the gift on the altar, turns back to the kneeling figure, and raises his hand in blessing. The person then rises, and steps back to his appointed place to the left or right of the altar, coming to a standstill just as the music ends. As the next verse begins, the next person enters the chancel. The movements should be made with deliberation and dignity, and so thoroughly rehearsed that keeping time to the music becomes instinctive, that the actor's mind may be on the expressing of the emotions of assurance that his gift will ring the chimes, and later disappointment that the chimes do not ring.

When it comes to Holger's turn to offer the pennies the music begins again as with the others, and accompanies the action through to the moment when the priest holds the pennies high above his head; here the organ and singing break off abruptly, the chimes ring out and keep pealing for a moment, without other music.

On the first note of the chimes the priest wheels swiftly, and with a commanding gesture signals the people grouped about the altar to their knees. He kneels also. The organ begins again, softly playing the final Alleluia. The angel enters from the right side, stands on the step of the altar, the central figure, —all about still kneeling awestruck. As the music continues the angel half sings, half chants the speeches, and underneath her voice, which should be as lovely as possible, come in the voices of the other singers very softly at first, like an echo from afar. As the angel's voice stops, those of the other singers grow into the great triumphant crescendo of the finale. Do not be afraid of holding this tableau while the music finishes. Indeed, none of the chancel scene should be hurried. Take it with great deliberation, and give whatever element is holding the scene at the moment (whether the action or the music) plenty of time to make its effect. The Alleluia is played through twice, once softly during the angel's singing, the second time in the triumphant climax. As this second singing ends, the lights on the chancel are blotted out, the back wall of the hut is replaced, the Old Woman disappears, the lights in the hut go up again, revealing Holger standing spellbound staring at the wall where the vision had been. As he turns to speak to the Woman, and during his final speeches, the organ plays softly as though from a great distance, and the chimes ring again, but not so loudly as before. This music continues till the front screens are brought together, and the play is over.

COSTUMES.—The costumes of this play are mediæval, picturesque, and easily constructed. The accompanying plates will give the best idea of their general appearance. The amounts of goods required for each are noted below.

First of all, in planning the costuming for a play a definite colour scheme should be decided on, with due regard for the scenery against which the colours are to stand out, and for the lights, which will greatly affect all values. Here is an opportunity for delightful study and the exercise of the highest artistic ability. Skilful lighting and a well-chosen background will make cheese-cloth as effective as cloth of gold. Taste and careful experimentation, not money, secure the best results.

Family ragbags will often yield excellent material for theatrical costumes, and of much better quality than would be bought new for the purpose. But if the stuff is to be purchased, two materials will be found especially suitable and inexpensive. For the peasants' costumes canton flannel is recommended, as it has body and comes in beautiful dark reds, browns, and other shades which light up well. For the dresses of the richer group in the chancel, sateen is best. It, too, comes in lovely colours, and has a very rich glossy finish, though to give variety an occasional piece of cheap velvet or upholstery brocade is very effective. For trimming these richer garments, bits of fur or passementerie can be used, or the material may be stencilled or even painted freehand. Large gold beads sewed on in a simple design give the appearance of rich embroidery, as do also flowers cut out of chintz and carefully pasted on.

All of the men's jerkins or tunics are made on the simple lines of a man's shirt, opened a little at the neck and belted in at the waist.

The most inexpensive tights for amateurs are well-fitting cotton underwear, dyed the desired colour. The children and Bertel can wear their own plain, soft, low-heeled slippers. The rich folk in the chancel wear their own slippers and draw on over them socks dyed to match the tights; these socks, if rolled down at the top, make a very passable substitute for the Romeo shoe of the period desired.

The following notes refer to the costumes of *Why the Chimes Rang,* as shown in the plates, the numbers corresponding to those given the figures therein. The estimates of the amount of goods required are all calculated on the basis of yard-wide goods for an adult of average size, except in the case of the two children, the costume of the older being planned for a fourteen-year-old boy, that of the younger for a child of ten.

1. *The Old Woman.*—Under robe, cut in straight simple lines, gracefully belted, 5½ yards; cloak and hood, 6 yards. If this cloak is black, or nearly so, it will help to conceal her entrance and exit, as black against black is practically invisible on the stage.

2. *Bertel.*—Jerkin, gaiters, and cap (all of same material), 3 yards; shirt (under jerkin), 2½ yards; cloak, 2½ yards. If preferred, Bertel's jerkin can be made with sleeves of the same goods instead of the white shirt showing as in the picture.

3. *Holger.*—Jerkin and cap, 1½ yards; cape, 2 yards.

4. *Steen.*—Jerkin and cap, 1½ yards; cape, 2 yards. It may be easier to lengthen the skirts of the boys' jerkins almost to the knee, and let them wear regular stockings and bloomers instead of tights. If long sleeves are preferred for them, a pair of stockings cut off at the ankle are easily attached at the arm hole, and make very good sleeves.

5. *The Angel.*—Outer robe, 7 yards; under robe, 5 yards.

This costume is best made of creamy cheese-cloth

over an under robe of the same, as cheese-cloth is faintly luminous in an intense light. It should be long enough to lie on the floor two or three inches all round, as a trailing effect is desirable.

6. *Rich Woman.*—Dress, 6 yards.

Her headdress is easily made of stiff white paper rolled up in cornucopia shape and sewed securely; over this a long white veil or scarf is draped.

7. *The Rich Man.*—Tunic, 2 yards; shirt, $2\frac{1}{2}$ yards; or $1\frac{1}{2}$ yards if the sleeves and neckpiece can be sewed right into the tunic, doing away with the under garment. If the costumes are to have repeated wear, it will be better to have the shirts made separate and of a washable material; they can then be cleansed more frequently than will be necessary for the tunics. The Rich Man's chain can be made of the heavy brass chain used for draping back curtains.

8. *The Priest.*—Under robe, $4\frac{1}{2}$ yards; outer robe, $6\frac{1}{2}$ yards. This costume will, of course, be greatly modified by the custom of the church of which he is supposed to be a representative.

9. *The King.*—Tunic, 2 yards; shirt, $2\frac{1}{2}$ yards; robe of office, $4\frac{1}{2}$ yards. The King's tunic in general cut is exactly like that of the other two courtiers (Nos. 7 and 12), but handsomer in material and trimming. The robe is just a straight piece that hangs from the shoulder and trails on the ground.

10. *Sage.*—Robe, 6 yards.

11. *Young Girl.*—Dress, 6 yards.

12. *Courtier.*—Tunic, 2 yards; shirt, $2\frac{1}{2}$ yards.

PROPERTIES.—The following list gives the properties needed in the play:

In the hut—

1. A porridge pot.
2. Three small bowls.
3. Three spoons. If pewter spoons are not to be had, wooden spoons can be bought cheaply.
4. Porridge. Custard or Spanish cream looks like

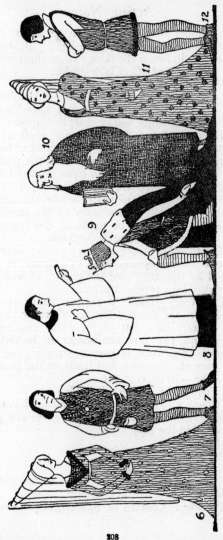

porridge, and is more easily eaten on the stage, but hot cream of wheat is also palatable if sweetened, and the steam from it will lend a touch of realism to the scene. It will save time to have it put in the three small bowls before the rise of the curtain, and the bowls can be covered with three little plates to keep the steam in till the food is wanted.

5. Two roughly made but substantial stools, one near the window, the other before the fire. Stools are better than chairs with backs, because they do not obstruct the view of the audience during the chancel scene.

6. Three large nails or wooden pegs in the walls strong enough to hold things, one on each side of the fireplace and one near the door. These would be impracticable with scenery made of screens, as any weight on the screen would pull it over. A solid wooden chest, such as a carpenter's tool chest, could be substituted to hold the children's wraps and the extra shawl for the Old Woman. The chest could be placed against the screen on the left or right as convenient.

7. Steen's cap and cape.

8. Holger's cap and cape.

9. The extra shawl Holger puts around the Old Woman.

10. Two bright pennies for Holger's gift.

11. Logs of firewood on the hearth. Not needed, of course, if the brazier is used instead of the fireplace.

In the chancel—

12. An altar cloth. This is properly a piece of fine linen edged with deep real lace. It should not be so wide as to cover the top of the altar, lest it obscure the light shining up through the hole. It should hang down in front of the altar and at the sides about eighteen inches. A very handsome-looking lace altar cloth can be cut from white paper.

13. Candlesticks.

14. Candles.

15. Two censers. Very passable censers can be made by swinging brass cups on the brass chains used for looping back curtains.

16. Incense.

17. Charcoal to burn the incense. (This comes in the box with the incense.)

18. Matches to light the incense.

19. The chimes (or the phonograph and record).

20. The organ.

Gifts to be put on the altar—

21. A chest full of gold coins for the Rich Man. (This chest should be about six by twelve inches, made of some polished wood. If difficult to find, substitute a money-bag of stout canvas for it.)

22. Gold coins for the Rich Man. These coins may be made of cardboard with gold paper pasted over them.

23. A gilded jewel box for the Courtier (this can be made from a cardboard box covered with gold paper).

24. Jewels to fill the gilded box. The smaller things that come for Christmas-tree decorations make very acceptable stage jewels.

25. A great book bound in vellum for the Sage to give. A heavy book can be covered with wrapping-paper the colour of vellum.

26. A pearl necklace.

27. A great sheaf of fresh lilies. These can be made at home of tissue paper, or very beautiful ones can be bought from the Dennison Manufacturing Company.

28. A golden crown. Made of cardboard coated with gold paper and set with Christmas-tree jewels. A more substantial crown can be made of thin sheet brass with all the edges turned like a hem, and trimmed with the inexpensive jewels which come for brass work.

Elizabeth A. McFadden.

ROBIN HOOD AND FRIAR TUCK

The play takes about twenty minutes in performance. There is no acting fee.

Unless it is rewritten by the form, or made part of
a Robin Hood programme, this play is hardly worth
formal production with dresses and properties. It
is, however, good fun to act in a corner of the
playing-fields, especially if there are trees and bushes
to serve as " wings."

The battle between the outlaws and the Friar's
men might be fought without weapons, the Friar's
first command being altered to " Down with your
clubs and staves," or it might be mimed.

See the notes on *Robin Hood and the Pedlar*.

ST. GEORGE AND THE DRAGON

This adaptation is copyright, but performances may
be given without payment or permission, provided
that the following notice is printed on the programme :

" This version of the old Christmas Mumming Play
is printed as an appendix to *Six Modern Plays*, and
is now performed by permission of the editor and
publishers, Mr. John Hampden and Messrs. Thomas
Nelson and Sons."

No setting is required, and the best possible costumes
and properties are simple, home-made ones. Sophisti-
cation will destroy the play. The Turkish Knight, for
instance, will look better in turban and flowing robes
improvised from towels of various colours, with an
aluminium-painted wooden scimitar, than in an expensive costume hired from London. The Dragon,
too, should have a home-made disguise. His head
may have a wire framework. Before entering, he
may roar through a lamp-chimney ; afterwards he
must rely upon his throat !

If another character is needed, the King of Egypt's daughter, the Princess Sabra, may be restored to her rightful place in the play and her hand formally bestowed upon St. George, who may be resplendent in a red-cross tabard, chain-mail sleeves (from an old jumper painted with aluminium paint), and wooden sword and shield. To reduce the cast the clown can easily be omitted, and the King of Egypt should be the next sacrifice.

A stage has been suggested, but if the audience is small enough the play may be given on the floor level as in the traditional country performances. In any case the audience should be caught up into the play as much as possible, and the speeches to the audience should be given whole-heartedly, not with a half-apologetic feeling that they are out of place. Young players will have no difficulty in this, however, and will probably find it easier than adults to act the play in the right spirit—that of a happy family party, in which the audience are part of the family.

SOME BOOKS FOR THE AMATEUR

Producing Plays. C. B. Purdom. Dent, 7s. 6d.

A Handbook for Producers and Players, by a leading amateur producer, which deals with all the activities of an amateur society, from rehearsal to business management.

Play Production for Amateurs. Rodney Bennett. Curwen, 2s. 6d. (Paper covers.)

An excellent and comprehensive little book.

The Small Stage and its Equipment. R. Angus Wilson, with an Introduction by Sir Barry Jackson. Allen and Unwin, 5s.

This deals with all the problems of temporary and permanent stage-construction, lighting and scenery as they confront schools and amateur societies, and it offers practicable solutions, with many diagrams.

Shakespeare for Community Players. Roy Mitchell. Dent, 6s.

The Bankside Costume Book. Melicent Stone. Wells Gardner, Darton, 3s.

These two books are excellent guides to costumes for the Robin Hood and the fairy-tale plays. The latter contains full instructions for dress-making, with diagrams.

British Costume during Nineteen Centuries, with an appendix on ecclesiastical costume. Mrs. Charles Ashdown. Nelson, 21s.

Costume and Fashion. Vol. II., 1066–1485. Herbert Norris. Dent, 31s. 6d.

A History of Everyday Things in England. Vol. I. M. and C. H. B. Quennell. Batsford, 8s. 6d.

Costume books, illustrated in colour and line, which are invaluable for reference.

A Book of Make-up. Eric Ward. Samuel French, 3s. 6d.

A practical handbook.

A List of Plays for Young Players, compiled by the Junior Plays Committee of the Village Drama Society. Nelson, 2s.

This list enumerates over 350 plays, with a summary of each, and the number of characters, settings, costumes, royalties, etc., so that it is a useful reference book for any amateur society.

Costumes can be hired very cheaply from the Village Drama Society, 274 New Cross Road, London, S.E.14.

PRINTED IN GREAT BRITAIN AT
THE PRESS OF THE PUBLISHERS

THE NELSON PLAYBOOKS

Edited by JOHN HAMPDEN, M.A.
Strong linen covers. 9*d*. each.

PLAY-READING and play-acting have never been so popular as they are to-day, but the price of plays is often a handicap to the play-reading circle and the amateur dramatic society, as well as to the individual reader or student. At NINEPENCE each the NELSON PLAYBOOKS do much to solve this difficulty. They will offer plays for all tastes, ranging from the liveliest farce to masterpieces of tragedy and comedy.

The Series is planned to include :

The best English plays of the past.
A selection of modern English plays.
Translations from classical and foreign drama.

Each has a very brief preface, designed to make the reader at home with the play, but not to trouble him with unnecessary details. In the plays by Shakespeare and other classical dramatists all difficult words and allusions are explained in very brief footnotes.

The paper is good, the print large and clear, and the margins are ample ; the bright, attractive covers, in a new design, are of strong linen which will render good service even " behind the scenes." And every play is carefully printed from a good text, expurgated where necessary.

Novel features of the series are the Cast List at the end of the book, with spaces for the players' names ; and a table showing the Distribution of Parts in small reading circles, so that if necessary one reader can take several parts without any clashing.

If the series continues to prove acceptable to a wide public the Publishers will extend it quickly and comprehensively.

THOMAS NELSON AND SONS, LTD.

THE NELSON PLAYBOOKS

LATEST ADDITIONS

202. FOUR MODERN PLAYS. Edited, with commentary and full acting notes, by John Hampden.

> Contents: "A Man of Ideas," a drama by Miles Malleson. "The Spinsters of Lushe," a costume comedy for six women or girls, by Philip Johnson. "The Theatre," a farcical comedy by H. F. Rubinstein. "Wayside War," a costume play by Margaret Napier.

These one-act plays are very easy to stage and effective in performance. "The Spinsters of Lushe" and "Wayside War" are now published for the first time. "A Man of Ideas" is specially suitable for a cast of men or senior boys.

119. MISS IN HER TEENS. By David Garrick, adapted by W. Graham Robertson.

A very lively and amusing farce in two acts, which can be played on a curtained stage. No acting fee. With the addition of a one-act play this makes an excellent evening's entertainment.

120. EVERYMAN; THE INTERLUDE OF YOUTH; THE WORLD AND THE CHILD.

These three beautiful old plays have been performed with great success by many amateur companies, young and old. They are now published in one volume for the first time, in good, modernized texts, and with full notes on acting and presentation.

201. PILGRIMS. By Rosalind Vallance. ENCHANTMENT. By Elsie Hayes. Two new one-act plays of distinction.

303. THE WOULD-BE NOBLEMAN. A new and vigorous translation by T. Watt of Molière's famous farcical comedy, *Le Bourgeois Gentilhomme.*

With acting notes and instructions for arranging an abridged version or single episodes.

For other titles see over.

THOMAS NELSON AND SONS, LTD.

THE NELSON PLAYBOOKS

(Plays now published for the first time are marked with an asterisk)

I. ENGLISH DRAMA (NON-COPYRIGHT)

100. SHE STOOPS TO CONQUER. By Oliver Goldsmith.
103. THE RIVALS. By R. B. Sheridan.
104. THE SCHOOL FOR SCANDAL. By R. B. Sheridan.
105. THE CRITIC. By R. B. Sheridan.
114. DOCTOR FAUSTUS. By Christopher Marlowe.
115. EVERY MAN IN HIS HUMOUR. By Ben Jonson.
116. THE KNIGHT OF THE BURNING PESTLE. By Beaumont and Fletcher.
118. STRAFFORD. By Robert Browning.
119. MISS IN HER TEENS.* By David Garrick. Adapted by W. Graham Robertson.
120. EVERYMAN, THE INTERLUDE OF YOUTH, THE WORLD AND THE CHILD. Edited, with full acting notes, by John Hampden.

II. ENGLISH DRAMA (COPYRIGHT)

200. MRS. ADIS *and* THE MOCKBEGGAR.* Two one-act plays by Sheila Kaye-Smith and John Hampden.
201. PILGRIMS.* By Rosalind Vallance.
    ENCHANTMENT.* By Elsie Hayes.
202. FOUR MODERN PLAYS. (See the previous page.)

III. CLASSICAL AND FOREIGN DRAMA

300. ANTIGONE. By Sophocles. Translated by Lewis Campbell.
301. THE WAY OF HONOUR* (Minna von Barnhelm). By Lessing. A new translation by E. U. Ouless.
302. THE MASTER BUILDER. By Henrik Ibsen. Translated by William Archer and Edmund Gosse.
303. THE WOULD-BE NOBLEMAN (Le Bourgeois Gentilhomme). By Molière. A new translation by T. Watt.
304. THE SEVEN AGAINST THEBES. By Æschylus. Translated by Edwyn Bevan.

IV. SHAKESPEARE

3. AS YOU LIKE IT.
15. JULIUS CÆSAR.
19. MACBETH.
21. THE MERCHANT OF VENICE.
23. A MIDSUMMER NIGHT'S DREAM.
31. THE TEMPEST.
35. TWELFTH NIGHT.

All the Shakespeare plays have very brief footnotes to explain difficult words and allusions, and are reasonably expurgated.

Nos. 201 and 302 are not intended for schools.

THOMAS NELSON AND SONS, LTD.
35-36 PATERNOSTER ROW, LONDON, E.C.4